MODERN
BIOLOGY
Teacher Manual

Dr. Rebecca Shelburne

MEMORIA PRESS

MEMORIA PRESS
www.MemoriaPress.com

MODERN BIOLOGY

TEACHER MANUAL
Dr. Rebecca Shelburne
ISBN 978-1-5477-0074-5

First Edition © 2019 Memoria Press | 0920

Cover illustration by Ernest Boar

CONTENTS

HOW TO USE THIS COURSE

Dear Students and Teachers,

Welcome to the wonderful world of *Modern Biology*. During this course, we will examine what cells are made up of and how they work. We will explore the world of microbes and viruses as well as plants and animals. Study of God's living world enables us to understand and use the Earth's resources to live as we've been directed by its very Creator. I think you will find this study to be one of the most interesting journeys you've yet to undertake in your studies and one of the most worthwhile topics to learn and master.

This course requires *Modern Biology* by Holt, Rinehart, and Winston, *Instructional Videos*, *Student Workbook*, *Teacher Manual*, *Tests*, and *Biology Coloring Workbook* (The Princeton Review). We also offer lesson plans.

TEXTBOOK
Modern Biology is a very large textbook and impossible to cover in one school year. I have chosen chapters for this course based on the linear progression of knowledge and what is important to understand before progressing on to more difficult topics. The omitted chapters have been left out either because they are very complex and better suited to a second-year biology course or because there is simply not time to cover them with any mastery for first-year biology students. Also, I assume that you have some prior study of physical science; if so, skip chapter 2. If this is not the case, you may want to read through chapter 2.

STUDENT WORKBOOK
It is important to read the textbook along with watching the instructional videos. I have laid out a study schedule in the lesson plans that recommends when to read the text and when to watch the video. Some students prefer to watch the video first and then read the text or vice versa. I recommend you do what works best for you. I have designed the lesson plans so that you spend about one hour per day on the course.

The *Student Workbook* provides you with a workspace to use the Glossary in the text to complete the vocabulary definitions for words found at the beginning of each section of a chapter. Answer the questions at the end of each section of a chapter on plain paper (or orally, if you prefer). Complete any assigned pages in the *Biology Coloring Workbook*. Fill out the study guide comprehension questions to prepare for the upcoming test and use as a study tool.

TEACHER MANUAL
The *Teacher Manual* contains answers to all questions as well as where to find the answer. Most answers are from *Modern Biology* (abbreviated MB), but others come from the *Biology Coloring Workbook* (abbreviated BCW) or the *Instructional Videos* (abbreviated IV). I have provided page numbers for the books and noted chapter and minute for the videos for easy reference.

TESTS
When grading the tests, I recommend counting each blank as one point (including the diagrams). For short answer questions, I have suggested how many points you may give.

I wish you well and hope that you find this course interesting, challenging, and enlightening.

Grace and Peace,
Dr. Rebecca Shelburne

FIRST
TRIMESTER

SECTION REVIEW KEY

Section 1

1. Biology is the study of every living thing. From medicine to food growth and development to air pollution, there is application in every area of life. (*Modern Biology* [MB], p. 5)

2. Biology improves life for humans, plants, and other animals. Society improves and becomes civilized because of what we know, what we are still learning, and how that knowledge is applied. (MB, p. 6)

3. All living things are made up of cells and exhibit organization. They grow and develop, they respond to stimuli, they exhibit metabolism and homeostasis, they reproduce, they change and evolve over time, and they exhibit movement at some point in their life cycle. (MB, p. 6)

4. Atoms bond together to form molecules. Molecules bond together to form organelles. Organelles organize into cells. Cells work together to form tissues. Tissues work together to form organs. Organs work together to form systems. Systems work together to form an organism. (MB, pp. 6-7)

5. Metabolism is the rate at which an organism turns nutrition or food into energy for cell function. Homeostasis is the narrow range at which most cells maintain their production and function to keep everything in the system in balance. Maintaining homeostasis requires energy from food, and so metabolism plays an important function in homeostasis. (MB, p. 8)

6. Living organisms grow by increasing the size and number of their cells. Nonliving things such as rocks can add mass but not increase in size by adding more cells. (MB, p. 8)

7. Most living cells are able to reproduce living cells identical to themselves, passing on the DNA or code for this process. This ensures the directions for reproduction are passed on for generations into perpetuity. (MB, p. 9)

CHAPTER 1: The Science of Life

SECTION 1 VOCABULARY

1. biology:

2. organization:

3. cell:

4. unicellular:

5. multicellular:

6. organ:

7. tissue:

8. organelle:

9. biological molecule:

10. homeostasis:

11. metabolism:

12. cell division:

13. development:

14. reproduction:

15. gene:

Section 2

1. All living organisms are made up of cells, they all share a common code in DNA, and they all adapt with time and environment change. (MB, pp. 10-11)

2. Unity and diversity are represented through phylogenetic diagrams and classification of organisms. (MB, pp. 10-11)

3. The domain Bacteria contains the kingdom Eubacteria. The domain Archaea contains the kingdom Archaebacteria. The domain Eukarya contains the kingdoms Protista, Fungi, Plantae, and Animalia. (MB, pp. 10-11)

4. Within an ecosystem, every organism is dependent on every other organism. If one disappears, it is likely the entire ecosystem will die. (MB, p. 11)

5. Evolution is supported by natural selection. The strongest of the species is the most likely to live and pass on the DNA that makes it strong, causing every generation to become better adapted to its environment until the species is varied enough to give it a new name because of its diversity. (MB, p. 11)

6. Natural selection, or the idea that the strongest or most well-adapted organism lives to pass on its DNA, is what drives evolution, which is the gradual change of a species until it has changed enough to warrant a new classification and its own name. (MB, p. 12)

COMPREHENSION QUESTIONS

1. Biology is the study of ___life or living organisms (MB, p. 5)___.

2. List the seven characteristics or qualities that constitute life and give an example of each.

    a. ___Cells and organization: Smallest unit of life organized into tissues and organ (MB, pp. 6-7)___

    b. ___Responsiveness: Pupils dilating in a dark room (MB, pp. 7-8)___

    c. ___Homeostasis: Sweating to maintain body temperature (MB, p. 8)___

    d. ___Metabolism: Converting food into energy for cell functions (MB, p. 8)___

    e. ___Growth and maturation (development): Cells taking in substances and cell differentiation (MB, p. 8)___

    f. ___Reproduction: Cell replication for growth or species reproduction (MB, p. 9)___

    g. ___Adaptation and change: The fastest animal catches the food and so lives to pass on favorable genes. (MB, p. 9)___

3. The smallest structural and functional unit of life is the ___cell (MB, p. 7)___

4. All living organisms exhibit structural and functional organization. Place the terms below in order from simplest to most complex and place an * by the term that indicates the simplest form of life.

Organisms	Tissues	Molecules	Organelles	Organs	Atoms	Cells	Systems

    a. ___Atoms (MB, p. 7)___   e. ___Tissues (MB, p. 7)___

    b. ___Molecules (MB, p. 7)___   f. ___Organs (MB, p. 7)___

    c. ___Organelles (MB, p. 7)___   g. ___Systems (MB, p. 7)___

    d. ___Cells* (MB, p. 7)___   h. ___Organisms (MB, p. 7)___

5. In which two ways can living organisms increase in size over time?

    a. ___Taking in molecules and other substances to increase cell size (MB, p. 8)___

    b. ___Adding more cells through cell replication to increase size (MB, p. 8)___

6. What are the two types of reproduction seen in living organisms, and how are they different?

    a. ___Asexual reproduction produces new identical cells or organisms. (MB, p. 9)___

    b. ___Sexual reproduction produces new and similar yet different cells or organisms. (MB, p. 9)___

7. Phylogenetic diagrams (Tree of Life) are used to help biologists classify (organize) organisms according to their similarities or common characteristics. There are many different classification systems; however, the system we will be using throughout the year organizes all living things into three domains. These domains are:

    a. ___Archaea (MB, pp. 10-11)___   b. ___Bacteria (MB, pp. 10-11)___   c. ___Eukarya (MB, pp. 10-11)___

8. The three domains are made up of six kingdoms. These six kingdoms and their domains are:

   a. _Archaea (MB, p. 11)_   Domain: _Archaea (MB, p. 11)_

   b. _Bacteria (MB, p. 11)_   Domain: _Bacteria (MB, p. 11)_

   c. _Protista (MB, p. 11)_   Domain: _Eukarya (MB, p. 11)_

   d. _Plantae (MB, p. 11)_   Domain: _Eukarya (MB, p. 11)_

   e. _Fungi (MB, p. 11)_   Domain: _Eukarya (MB, p. 11)_

   f. _Animalia (MB, p. 11)_   Domain: _Eukarya (MB, p. 11)_

9. Kingdoms are then made up of different _phyla (MB, p. 339)_.

10. Number the terms below in order from the most general to the most specific. (See text, p. 338)

    _5_ Order   _1_ Domain   _7_ Genus   _4_ Class

    _8_ Species   _3_ Phylum   _2_ Kingdom   _6_ Family

11. All organisms within a defined geographic area are in relationship with each other in some way or another. This relationship is termed _interdependence (Instructional Video [IV], Chapter 1, Minute 31)_

12. The defined geographic area in which organisms are dependent on each other and interact is called an _ecosystem (MB, p. 11)_.

13. The specific study of these organisms and their homes is called _ecology (MB, p. 11)_.

14. All living organisms must reproduce in order for the species to survive. Hereditary information is passed from one organism to another in the form of _genes or DNA (MB, p. 11)_.

15. Favorable hereditary traits that allow a species to live and reproduce more successfully are passed from one generation to another. This process is termed _natural selection (MB, p. 12)_.

16. Natural selection occurs over time, causing new and genetically different species to emerge. This process is called _evolution or change over time (MB, p. 12)_.

17. The steps in the process of scientific inquiry (the scientific method) are listed below. Briefly describe or explain each step on the line provided. Theory is completed for you.

    a. Theory: A well-tested and accepted explanation or model of the natural world

    b. Observation: _Noticing something in the natural world that causes a question to be raised (MB, p. 13)_

    c. Hypothesis: _A proposed answer or explanation to the question raised (MB, p. 13)_

    d. Prediction: _The expected outcome of an experiment (MB, p. 13)_

    e. Experiment: _A test performed to support the hypothesis (MB, p. 13)_

    f. Results: _Quantitative findings of the experiment (MB, p. 13)_

    g. Analysis: _Objective data calculations and outcomes (MB, p. 13)_

    h. Conclusions: _Determination if the original hypothesis and theory are supported or not (MB, p. 13)_

18. Study the "Parts of a Microscope" diagram in the Appendix of this guide. Then label the parts of the simple compound light microscope below.

a. Ocular (MB, p. 21)

b. Objectives (MB, p. 21)

c. Stage (MB, p. 21)

d. Arm (MB, p. 21)

e. Coarse focus knob (MB, p. 21)

f. Fine focus knob (MB, p. 21)

g. Light source (MB, p. 21)

h. Power source (MB, p. 21)

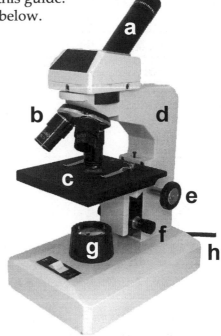

19. Review base and derived units.

a. What is the base unit for distance? meter (MB, p. 23)

b. What is the base unit for time? second (MB, p. 23)

c. What is the derived unit for volume? cubic meter (MB, p. 23)

d. What is the base unit for mass? kilogram (MB, p. 23)

e. What is the accepted unit for temperature? Celsius (MB, p. 23)

f. What are the derived units for density? kg/m³ (MB, p. 23)

20. Review SI metric prefixes and fill in the abbreviation and value for each. (MB, p. 23)

Prefix	Abbreviation	Value
giga	G	1,000,000,000
mega	M	1,000,000
kilo	k	1,000
hecto	h	100
deka	da	10
base unit	none	1
deci	d	1/10
centi	c	1/100
milli	m	1/1,000
micro	μ	1/1,000,000
nano	n	1/1,000,000,000
pico	p	1/1,000,000,000,000

SECTION REVIEW KEY

Section 1

1. Organic compounds contain carbon. These compounds form covalent bonds with themselves and other atoms. There are a few exceptions such as carbon dioxide, which contains carbon but is considered an inorganic compound. (MB, p. 51)

2. Carbon is able to bond covalently to four other atoms, compounds, or molecules, allowing it to take on different properties, shapes, and functions. (MB, p. 51)

3. Hydroxyl, carboxyl, amino, and phosphate (MB, p. 52)

4. Functional groups influence the characteristics (shape, pH, solubility, function, etc.) of the molecule. (MB, p. 52)

5. Polymers form through condensation reactions involving two or more monomers of either the same or different monomers. Macromolecules are large polymers. (MB, p. 53)

6. Polymers are broken down by hydrolysis reactions liberating individual monomers or groups of monomers. (MB, p. 53)

7. The removal of a phosphate group from ATP releases energy to start and complete other molecular reactions. (MB, p. 54)

8. Answers will vary. Water is the medium in which all chemical reactions occur. It is also the essential building block of many molecules. (MB, pp. 52-53)

9. Answers will vary. Most organic compounds contain both carbon and hydrogen bonded together. Because carbon dioxide does not contain hydrogen bonded to carbon, it is classified as an inorganic compound. (MB, pp. 51-52)

10. Because water is being removed, the term dehydration accurately describes the loss of water from the two molecules being joined by the reaction. (MB, p. 53)

VOCABULARY

Section 1

1. organic compound: _____

2. functional group: _____

3. monomer: _____

4. polymer: _____

5. macromolecule: _____

6. condensation reaction: _____

7. hydrolysis: _____

8. adenosine triphosphate (ATP): _____

Section 2

9. carbohydrate: _____

10. monosaccharide: _____

11. disaccharide: _____

12. polysaccharide: _____

13. protein: _____

14. amino acid: _____

15. peptide bond: _____

16. polypeptide: _____

12   Chapter 3: Biochemistry

17. enzyme:_____

18. substrate: _____

19. active site:_____

20. lipid: _____

21. fatty acid: _____

22. phospholipid: _____

23. wax: _____

24. steroid: _____

25. nucleic acid: _____

26. deoxyribonucleic acid (DNA): _____

27. ribonucleic acid (RNA): _____

28. nucleotide: _____

Biology Coloring Workbook

Complete Chapter 1: Carbohydrates, Lipids, Proteins; Chapter 4: Structure of DNA.

Section 2

1. A monosaccharide is a single monomer of sugar containing carbon, hydrogen, and oxygen in a 1:2:1 ratio. A disaccharide is a sugar made up of two monosaccharides, and a polysaccharide is a sugar made up of three or more monosaccharides. (MB, pp. 55-56)

2. Amino acids are joined together by peptide bonds through condensation reactions. A protein is formed when many amino acids bond together. (MB, p. 56)

3. The twenty different amino acids differ only in the R group bonded to the central carbon atom. (MB, p. 56)

4. Enzyme action occurs when a substrate that is specific to the enzyme bonds to it and causes the enzyme's shape to change, reducing the energy required to catalyze the reaction. (MB, p. 57)

5. Because phospholipids have a hydrophilic component and a hydrophobic component. When they are in a water environment, they line up so the hydrophobic fatty acid tails are shielded from the water and the hydrophilic glycerol heads are on the insides and outsides, creating a lipid bilayer membrane that is hydrophilic on either side. (MB, p. 59)

6. Triglycerides or dietary fats are composed of a glycerol molecule bonded to three fatty acid chains. A phospholipid or cell membrane lipid is composed of a glycerol molecule bonded to two fatty acids and a phosphate group. Waxes and sterols are simple fatty acid chains or carbon ring structures. (MB, pp. 59-60)

7. DNA maintains and stores all of the genetic information of the cell, and RNA carries the codes for protein synthesis and can act as an enzyme. (MB, p. 60)

8. Energy from carbohydrates is stored in muscles as glycogen. Glycogen can easily be broken down into glucose for quick energy. (MB, pp. 55-56)

9. Heat weakens bonds between amino acids, changing the protein's shape as the peptide bonds are broken. (MB, pp. 56-57)

10. More plants such as nuts, avocados, and olive oils and less meat fat, butter, and dairy foods (MB, p. 59)

COMPREHENSION QUESTIONS

1. Atoms of different elements bond together to form ___compounds (MB, p. 51)___.

2. Which four elements make up 90% of all living organisms?
   Carbon, oxygen, hydrogen, and nitrogen (IV, Chapter 3.1 Part 1, Minute 3)

3. Since these four elements are all nonmetals, what type of bonds will they form to build the molecules that make up living systems? ___Covalent (MB, p. 51)___

4. Organic compounds all contain ___carbon (MB, p. 51)___, while inorganic compounds do not.

5. How many valence electrons does carbon have? ___Four (MB, p. 51)___

6. How many covalent bonds does carbon need to form to be neutral and stable? ___Four (MB, p. 51)___

7. What three types of functional structures can carbon molecules form? Draw an example of each.

a. Straight chains (MB, p. 51)	b. Branched chains (MB, p. 51)	c. Rings (MB, p. 51)
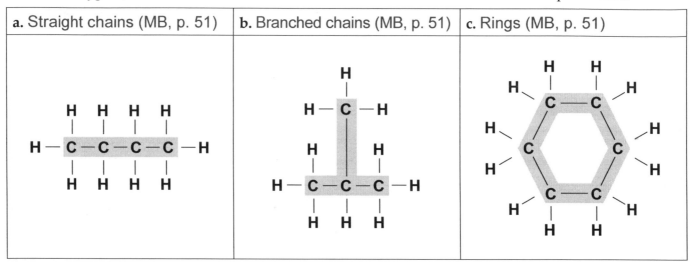		

8. What is a functional group?
   Special groups of atoms chemically bonded together that influence the characteristics of the compounds they bond to and the types of reactions those compounds undergo. (MB, p. 52)

9. What are the four functional groups most commonly seen in organic molecules?
   Any compound an -OH group bonds to becomes polar. (MB, p. 52)

Draw the structure of each one and its chemical formula.

a. Hydroxyl -OH	b. Carboxyl CO_2H	c. Amino NH_2	d. Phosphate PO_4
—OH	$\overset{\displaystyle O}{\underset{\displaystyle \\| }{}}$ —C—OH	H — —N—H	O ‖ —O—P—OH | OH

10. A simple carbon molecule that forms the base of larger molecules is called a ___monomer (MB, p. 53)___.

11. Two or more functionally similar monomers bond together to form ___polymers (MB, p. 53)___.

12. Large polymers form the four fundamental macromolecules that make up all living organisms. List these four macromolecules and give an example of each.

a. _Carbohydrates_ Example: Any sugar (potatoes, carrots, rice, wheat, glucose) (MB, pp. 55-56)

b. _Proteins_ Example: Muscle meats, eggs, etc. (MB, pp. 56-57)

c. _Lipids_ Example: Butter, lard, cooking oil, etc. (MB, pp. 59-60)

d. _Nucleic acids_ Example: DNA or RNA (MB, p. 60)

13. Each of these macromolecules is formed by bonding one or more monomers together. The type of reaction that occurs to bond monomers into macromolecules is called a _condensation reaction (MB, p. 53)_ .

14. What molecule is liberated every time two monomers bond together? Water (MB, p. 53)

15. Often, macromolecules or smaller polymers must be broken down into monomers for the organism's use. The reverse reaction that breaks polymers into monomers is called a _hydrolysis reaction (MB, p. 53)_ .

16. Both of these reactions require energy. In fact, all reactions in living systems require energy at the cell level. The energy produced by cells to fuel cell reactions is called ATP (MB, p. 54) What does this acronym stand for? _Adenosine triphosphate (MB, p. 54)_

17. Cells make ATP from the carbohydrates they consume. What are the monomers and functional groups making up one molecule of ATP?

Sugar ribose , _adenine_ , and _three phosphate groups (MB, p. 54)_ .

18. What occurs during the hydrolysis of ATP to liberate energy?
One phosphate group is cleaved from ATP. (MB, p. 54)

19. What are the products and reactants in this reaction?

a. Reactants: ATP and water (MB, p. 54)

b. Products: ADP (adenosine diphosphate), one phosphate group, and energy (MB, p. 54)

Let's talk about CARBOHYDRATES (AKA Sugars).

20. Most sugars, also called carbohydrates, are made up of simple repeating monomers specifically called _monosaccharides (MB, p. 55)_ .

21. What three elements make up these monomers of sugar and in what ratio? $C = 6$, $H = 12$, and $O = 6$ (MB, p. 55)

22. The chemical formula for a simple monomer of sugar is _$C_6H_{12}O_6$ (MB, p. 55)_ .

23. What are the three most common monosaccharides (monomers of sugar), and where are they found?

a. _Glucose: Found in most plant products and is the monosaccharide that provides energy for ATP (MB, p. 55)_

b. _Fructose: Found in fruits (MB, p. 55)_

c. _Galactose: Found in dairy products (MB, p. 55)_

24. These monosaccharides all have the same chemical formula, $C_6H_{12}O_6$, but are all very different compounds. What is the term used to describe this relationship?
They are isomers. (MB, p. 55)

25. Two monosaccharides bond together to form a <u>disaccharide (MB, p. 56)</u>.

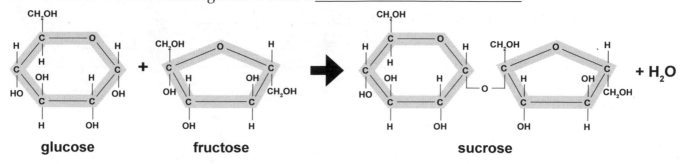

glucose   **fructose**   **sucrose**   + H₂O

26. Three or more monosaccharides bonded together form a <u>polysaccharide (MB, p. 56)</u>.

27. Glucose is stored by all organisms so it is readily available to make ATP when cells need energy. Plants store glucose as <u>starch (MB, p. 56)</u> and/or <u>cellulose (MB, p. 56)</u> while the storage form of glucose in animals is called <u>glycogen (MB, p. 56)</u>. These are all examples of polysaccharides.

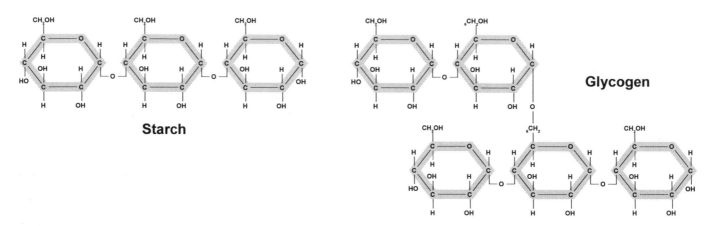

Starch   **Glycogen**

Let's talk about PROTEINS.

28. What are the monomers called that build proteins? <u>Amino acids (AA) (MB, p. 56)</u>

29. How many different amino acids are found in the proteins that make up living systems? <u>20 (MB, p. 56)</u>

30. What are the structural components of each amino acid?
<u>Central carbon atom, a carboxyl group, an amino group, a hydrogen atom, and a variable</u>
<u>(R) (MB, p. 56)</u>

31. Draw the basic molecular structure of an amino acid.

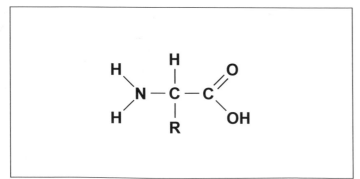

(MB, p. 56)
(*Biology Coloring Workbook* [BCW], p. 19)

32. The covalent bond that forms between two amino acids is called a _____ peptide bond (MB, p. 57).

33. Two amino acids bonded together are called a dipeptide (MB, p. 57)_____ .

34. Three or more amino acids bonded together are called a polypeptide (MB, p. 57)_____ .

35. One or more polypeptides joined together in a specific configuration can be called a protein (MB, p. 57)

36. All cells make proteins. It is the primary work of every cell to produce proteins specific to that cell type. Name a few different examples of proteins made by the human body.

Hormones, enzymes, etc. (MB, p. 57)_____

37. Proteins made by most cells that catalyze (start or speed up) reactions are called enzymes (MB, p. 57)

38. Describe the action of an enzyme using the pictures provided.

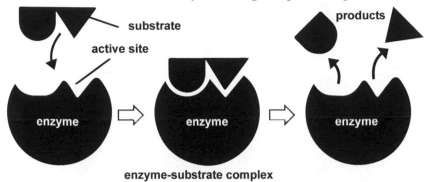

The compound (substrate) binds to the enzyme on the specific binding site. The enzyme changes shape, thereby weakening or aligning the compound to be bonded or broken, reducing the energy needed to form or break a bond. This process may proceed in either direction. (MB, p. 57)

39. The hormone insulin is another example of a protein produced by cells of an animal's pancreas. If this hormone (protein) is not effective or insufficient, what disease process occurs? Diabetes (MB, p. 58)

40. What is the primary function of insulin?

To aid glucose moving from the blood into the body cells for use (MB, p. 58)

41. Fill in the table below with the correct terms associated with the different types of diabetes. (MB, p. 58)

	Type 1 Diabetes	**Type 2 Diabetes**
Onset	Juvenile	Adult
Cause	Genetic	Poor diet and exercise
Management	Synthetic insulin injections	Diet and exercise
% Cases in the U.S.	5-10%	90-95%

Let's talk about LIPIDS (AKA Fats).

42. Fats or lipids are large, nonpolar (hydrophobic) organic molecules and most are made up of the monomer called a ___fatty acid (MB, p. 59)___ .

43. This monomer is a varying length ___hydrocarbon (MB, p. 59)___ chain as shown below.

Each carbon atom may be saturated with hydrogen or some hydrogen may be removed, causing carbon to form a double bond with an adjacent carbon. The more carbon atoms without hydrogen atoms, the more unsaturated the fat becomes and is said to be a polyunsaturated fat.

44. Saturated fats are usually ___solid (MB, p. 59)___ at room temperature. An example is ___butter (MB, p. 59)___ .

45. Unsaturated fats are usually ___liquid (MB, p. 59)___ at room temperature. An example is ___olive oil (MB, p. 59)___

46. Lipids are sorted into four main categories based on structure and function. List each category and briefly describe the function or purpose of each.

    a. ___Triglycerides___
       ___Function: Dietary fats found in some plants and most animals (MB, p. 59)___

    b. ___Phospholipids___
       ___Function: Fats that make up the plasma membrane of every cell (MB, p. 59)___

    c. ___Waxes___
       ___Function: Typically seen where waterproofing is needed (MB, p. 60)___

    d. ___Steroids (Sterols)___
       ___Function: Carbon rings making up some hormones and cholesterol (MB, p. 60)___

47. What is the structural difference between a triglyceride and a phospholipid?
    ___A triglyceride is made up of one glycerol molecule and three fatty acid chains, while phospholipids___
    ___are made up of a glycerol molecule, two fatty acids, and a phosphate group. (MB, p. 59)___

48. Draw the basic chemical structures of the following: (BCW, p. 17) (IV, Ch. 3.2 Pt. 2, Min. 2)

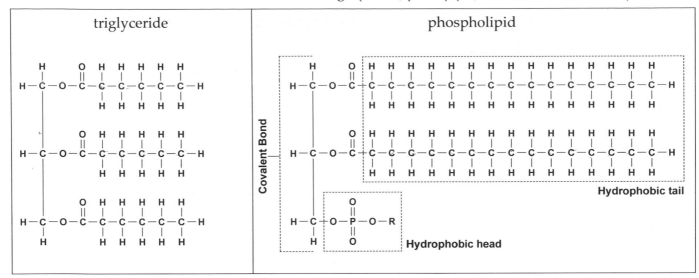

| triglyceride | phospholipid |

49. Using the diagrams below, explain the significance of the structural components of phospholipids and how the design of the phospholipid ideally suits its function.

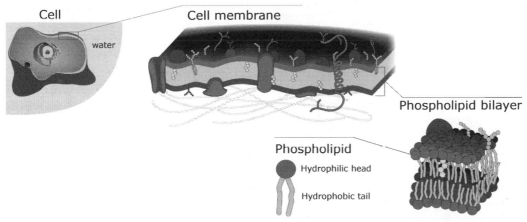

The phosphate heads are hydrophilic and so line the inside and the outside of the plasma membrane where they are next to a water environment. The fatty acid tails are hydrophobic and make up the interior of the membrane, which aids in the control of substances entering and exiting the cell. (MB, p. 59)

50. The group of lipids known as sterols or steroids are not made up of fatty acids but rather ___carbon rings (MB, p. 60)___.

Let's talk about NUCLEIC ACIDS (DNA and RNA).

51. What are the two primary functions of nucleic acids?
- a. ___Store and transfer genetic information (MB, p. 60)___
- b. ___Direct and control cell activities and processes (MB, p. 60)___

52. What does the acronym DNA stand for? ___Deoxyribonucleic Acid (MB, p. 60)___

53. What does the acronym RNA stand for? ___Ribonucleic Acid (MB, p. 60)___

54. The monomer making up both nucleic acids is called a <u>nucleotide (MB, p. 60)</u>

55. The spiral staircase structure that DNA nucleotides form is called a <u>double helix (IV Ch. 3.2 Pt. 2, Min. 16)</u>.

56. What are the three compounds/functional groups making up each nucleic acid?

<u>A sugar (ribose or deoxyribose), a phosphate group, and the variable called a nitrogen base (MB, p. 60)</u>

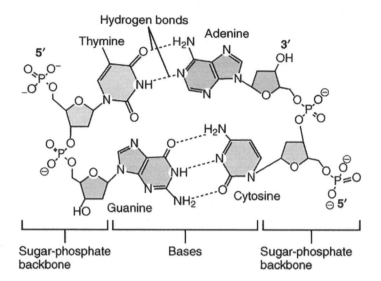

A DNA molecule is made up of four different repeating nucleotides forming two strands that are held together by hydrogen bonds. The figure to the left shows a small segment of DNA made up of four separate nucleotides. An average gene is composed of one thousand or more nucleotides.

57. What is a gene?

<u>A segment of DNA (a series of nucleotides) that code for a cell process or a hereditary trait (IV, Ch. 3.2 Pt. 2, Min. 19-20)</u>

58. Approximately how many genes make up each human genome? <u>30,000 (IV, Ch. 3.2 Pt. 2, Min. 21)</u>

CHAPTER 4: Cell Structure and Function

VOCABULARY

Section 1

1. cell: _____ *watch yartube*

2. cell theory: _____

Section 2

3. plasma membrane: _____

4. cytoplasm: _____

5. cytosol: _____

6. nucleus: _____

7. prokaryote: _____

8. eukaryote: _____

9. organelle: _____

10. tissue: _____

11. organ: _____

12. organ system: _____

Section 3

13. phospholipid bilayer: _____

14. chromosome: _____

15. nuclear envelope: _____

SECTION REVIEW KEY

Section 1

[Skip #1-3.]

4. Cell theory states: All living things are made of cells, the cell is the basic functional and structural unit of all living systems, and all cells come from other cells. (MB, p. 70)

5. The first dead (cork) cells were observed by Robert Hooke. Living cells were observed by Anton van Leeuwenhoek. Cell theory was established. (MB, pp. 70-71)

6. All living things are made up of cells. They exhibit organization, homeostasis, reproduction, growth and development, metabolism, movement, change over time, and response to stimuli. (MB, p. 71)

Section 2

1. A cell's shape and size are always influenced, if not determined, by the cell's function. Cells that are protective, like skin cells, are flat and hard like tiny shields. Cells that secrete substances are shaped like large cubes or columns to hold the substances they secrete. Cells that transmit, such as nerve cells, have long extensions to carry the electrical signal great distances. (MB, p. 72-73)

2. A cell's surface area will always limit the cell's growth and thereby its volume. Since a cell must move nutrients and gasses to its core, the smaller it is, the easier it is for the cell to utilize its cell membrane surface area to move nutrients in and waste products out. (MB, p. 73)

3. The three basic parts that are similar in all eukaryotic cells are the cell membrane, the cytoplasm, and the nucleus. (MB, p. 74)

4. Prokaryotic cells lack a membrane-bound nucleus, lack membrane-bound organelles, and are usually much smaller than eukaryotic cells. (MB, p. 75)

5. Cells, tissues, organs, and systems (MB, p. 76)

6. Its volume would increase from 1 cubic centimeter to 27 cubic centimeters. (MB, p. 73)

7. All cells require a blueprint or instructions to run the activity of the cell (nucleus), all cells need a liquid medium for reactions to occur (cytoplasm), and all cells need a way to control what gets into and out of the cell (plasma membrane). (MB, pp. 74-75)

8. Prokaryotic cells contain genetic material in their nucleoid, which is simply not bound by a membrane. (MB, p. 75)

Section 3

1. Since the cell membrane is primarily a fluid environment, it allows the phospholipids, proteins, and sterols to move around the membrane as needed, creating a constantly changing mosaic. (MB, p. 78)

2. The DNA is stored and protected, templates to synthesize proteins are constructed from the DNA, and one subunit of the ribosome is constructed. (MB, p. 79)

3. The nucleus stores and protects DNA, mitochondria produce ATP to power the cell, ribosomes serve as the site for protein synthesis, the endoplasmic reticulum serves to assemble proteins and lipids as well as act as an intracellular highway system, the Golgi apparatus packages and directs synthesized molecules, and lysosomes break down worn-out cell parts. (MB, pp. 79-82)

4. Mitochondria have a lipid bilayer membrane and their own DNA for self-replication. (MB, p. 80)

5. The cytoskeleton is made up of microtubules containing the protein tubulin, and they

function in movement and maintaining cell shape. Microfilaments are made of the protein actin and function in cell division, maintaining cell structure and cell movement. Intermediate filaments are fibrous proteins that help to anchor the nucleus and other organelles as well as maintain cell shape. (MB, p. 84)

6. Many mitochondria, since cells that move a lot would require more energy, which mitochondria produce in the form of ATP (MB, p. 80)

7. Because mitochondria have their own DNA and can self-replicate, it is thought that they were once smaller prokaryotic cells that were engulfed by larger prokaryotic cells. This would have given protection to the smaller cell, and the smaller cell would have provided energy for the larger cell, creating a symbiotic relationship and the first eukaryotic cell. (MB, p. 80)

8. Organelles are all held in place by the cytoskeleton, which controls and restricts their movement throughout the cell. (MB, p. 84)

Section 4

1. Plant cells have one or two cell walls in addition to the plasma membrane, they have a central water or contractile vacuole to help them manage extra water, and they have multiple different types of plastids. (MB, p. 87)

2. The plasma membrane is a phospholipid bilayer just like all cell membranes. The primary cell wall is made up of cellulose outside the plasma membrane and synthesized by the plasma membrane. The secondary cell wall forms in cells of woody plants between the primary cell wall and the plasma membrane. The secondary cell wall is usually produced when the cell has stopped growing and forms wood. (MB, p. 88)

3. Plastid is a general term for a plant cell organelle that has its own DNA and can replicate itself. Chloroplasts are one type of plastid that contain chlorophyll and function in photosynthesis. Chromoplasts contain several different color pigments that also aid in photosynthesis. Amyloplasts are specialized plastids for storing excess sugars as starch in some plants like potatoes. (MB, p. 89)

4. Vacuoles are different from plastids as they do not have their own DNA. Water or contractile vacuoles store water. Some vacuoles store toxins or oils such as poison

16. nucleolus: _____

17. ribosome: _____

18. mitochondrion: _____

19. endoplasmic reticulum: _____

20. Golgi apparatus: _____

21. lysosome: _____

22. cytoskeleton: _____

23. microtubule: _____

24. microfilament: _____

25. cilium: _____

26. flagellum: _____

27. centriole: _____

Section 4

28. cell wall: _____

29. central vacuole: _____

30. plastid: _____

31. chloroplast: _____

32. thylakoid: _____

33. chlorophyll: _____

ivy, and some store compounds such as nicotine in tobacco plants. Some plants store colorful pigments in vacuoles. (MB, p. 88)

5. A prokaryotic cell is distinguished from a eukaryotic cell by its lack of membrane-bound organelles and a membrane-bound nucleus. Plant cells are distinguished from animal cells by their cell walls; plastids, especially chloroplasts; and their central vacuole. (MB, pp. 87-88)

6. The central vacuole plays a much more important role. When the central vacuole is full, the plant stands upright. When it is empty, the plant droops. The cell wall remains in either case. The cell wall gives the cell itself shape and structure, but the shape of the plant itself is influenced more by the fullness of the central vacuole. (MB, p. 88)

7. First, find out if the cell is prokaryotic or eukaryotic by determining if it has membrane-bound organelles and a membrane-bound nucleus. If it is eukaryotic, determine if it is plant or animal by the presence or absence of chloroplasts, a cell wall, and a central vacuole. (MB, pp. 87-90)

8. Plant toxins are produced by the cell and stored in vacuoles. These vacuoles keep the plant safe from the toxins it produces. (MB, p. 48)

Biology Coloring Workbook

Complete Chapter 2: The Animal Cell, The Plant Cell.

COMPREHENSION QUESTIONS

1. What are the three major tenets of cell theory?
   a. _Every living organism is made up of cells. (MB, p. 70)_
   b. _The cell is the smallest structural and functional unit of life. (MB, p. 70)_
   c. _All cells come from other cells. (MB, p. 70)_

2. Which scientist was the first to observe dead cells and name them? _Robert Hooke (MB, p. 69)_

3. Which scientist first observed living algae cells? _Anton van Leeuwenhoek (MB, p. 70)_

4. A cell's shape, size, and organization are determined by the cell's _function (MB, p. 72)_.

5. What is the size of an average cell? _10-50µ (MB, p. 73)_

6. Explain why cells tend to be small.
   A cell can only grow as large as it is able to deliver nutrients to the innermost cell structures across its outer surface area. Smaller volume with increased surface area allows the cell to more efficiently deliver nutrition to its center. (Surface area: volume ratio) (MB, p. 73)

7. Which three structures are common to all cells?
   Plasma membrane, DNA, cytoplasm and its contents (MB, p. 74)

8. What is the primary purpose of the cell's plasma membrane?
   Control of substances entering and exiting the cell (MB, p. 74)

9. What are the three primary components of cytoplasm?
   Cytosol, cytoskeleton, and organelles except the nucleus (MB, p. 74)

10. What is found inside a cell's nucleus?
    Nucleoplasm, DNA, and the nucleolus (MB, p. 74)

11. What are two main features that distinguish a prokaryotic cell from a eukaryotic cell?
    A membrane-bound nucleus and membrane-bound organelles (MB, p. 75)

12. Since prokaryotic cells have no membrane-bound nucleus, where is the DNA found?
    Nucleoid (MB, p. 75)

13. Which two organismal kingdoms make up the group of organisms called prokaryotes?
    a. _Archaea (MB, p. 75)_
    b. _Bacteria (MB, p. 75)_

14. Which four organismal kingdoms make up the domain of organisms classified as eukaryotes?

a. Protista (MB, p. 75) (IV, Chapter 4.2, Minute 12)

b. Fungi (MB, p. 75) (IV, Chapter 4.2, Minute 12)

c. Plantae (MB, p. 75) (IV, Chapter 4.2, Minute 12)

d. Animalia (MB, p. 75) (IV, Chapter 4.2, Minute 12)

15. Organisms may be a single cell living independently. These organisms are said to be __unicellular__.
Identical cells living in a group without any cell specialization are said to be __colonial__.
Groups of cells living together with cell specialization are said to be __multicellular__ (IV, Ch. 4.2, Min. 12-15)

16. List three functions of the cell membrane.

a. Controls which substances can move into and out of the cell (MB, p. 77)

b. Gives the cell shape and protection (MB, p. 77)

c. Allows the inside of the cell to communicate with the outside (MB, p. 77)

17. List the three primary types of molecules found in a typical cell membrane and briefly state the function of each.

a. Phospholipids Function: Form a barrier and control substances entering (MB, p. 77)

b. Proteins Function: Enzymes, communication, and transport (MB, p. 78)

c. Sterols Function: Insulate and give shape (MB, p. 77)

18. Peripheral plasma membrane proteins are typically __enzymes (MB, p. 78)__ that catalyze reactions or __cell surface markers (MB, p. 78)__ that identify the cell to surrounding cells.

19. Integral plasma membrane proteins are embedded in the membrane and usually extend through to both sides. These proteins typically act as __docking stations (MB, p. 78)__ that bind substances the cell may need or __transport proteins (MB, p. 78)__ that shield molecules from the phospholipid bilayer as they are moved into or out of the cell.

20. The cell membrane is a very liquid, changeable environment. Proteins, sterols, and phospholipids move laterally through the membrane as needed. This model is called a __fluid mosaic (MB, p. 78)__.

Eukaryotic Cell Organelles

21. The nuclear contents are enclosed in a membrane made up of a dual layer of __phospholipids (MB, p. 79)__

22. The nuclear membrane contains proteins embedded for the transport of substances across the membrane. These proteins are specifically called __nuclear pores (MB, p. 79)__.

23. Within the nucleus, DNA is found in the form of __chromatin (MB, p. 79)__ if the cell is not replicating and __chromosomes (MB, p. 79)__ if the cell is preparing to divide.

24. The jellylike substance in which the DNA is suspended is called __nucleoplasm (MB, p. 79)__.

25. The smaller organelle within the nucleus where DNA is concentrated for the purpose of making ribosomal RNA is called the __nucleolus (MB, p. 79)__.

26. Label the nuclear structures on the diagram below.

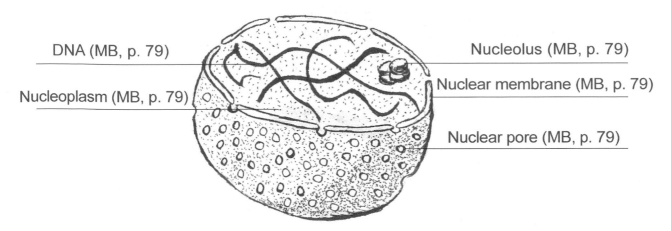

DNA (MB, p. 79)

Nucleolus (MB, p. 79)

Nucleoplasm (MB, p. 79)

Nuclear membrane (MB, p. 79)

Nuclear pore (MB, p. 79)

27. The primary purpose of the mitochondria is to convert glucose (MB, p. 80) into ATP (MB, p. 80)

28. Mitochondria can produce new mitochondria because they have their own DNA (MB, p. 80)

29. The mitochondria is made up of two layers of phospholipids (MB, p. 80) that form an external membrane and internal folds called cristae (MB, p. 80).

30. Ribosomes are made up of two smaller subunits. One subunit is assembled in the nucleolus and is made up of RNA (MB, p. 80) and the other subunit is a protein (MB, p. 80).

31. What is the primary purpose of the ribosome?
Assembles amino acids into proteins (MB, p. 80)

32. Where in the cell are ribosomes found?
Free floating in the cytoplasm or attached to rough endoplasmic reticulum (MB, p. 80)

33. The endoplasmic reticulum (ER) is composed of a phospholipid bilayer that forms a membranous tubular highway system within a cell for synthesis and transport. Rough endoplasmic reticulum works in the synthesis of proteins (MB, p. 81) and is rough because it is covered with ribosomes (MB, p. 81).

34. Smooth endoplasmic reticulum is not covered with ribosomes and functions in the synthesis and transport of lipids (MB, p. 81).

35. The Golgi apparatus is another system of phospholipid tubes that function in the packaging, marking, and transport of vesicles produced by the endoplasmic reticulum. (MB, p. 82)

36. Different cells produce different types of vesicles based on the cell's purpose. Describe the formation and structure of any vesicle.
Tobacco plants produce vesicles containing nicotine, some plant cells produce vesicles containing colorful pigments, etc. (MB, pp. 83, 88)

37. What is the purpose of lysosomes?
They secrete digestive enzymes to break down worn-out organelles, other vesicles containing harmful substances, microbes, or even whole damaged cells. (MB, p. 82)

38. What is the purpose of peroxisomes? The neutralization of free radicals (MB, p. 83)

39. What are two primary functions of the cytoskeleton?

   a. Gives the cell shape and holds organelles in place (MB, p. 84)

   b. Intracellular movement (MB, p. 84)

40. What are the three types of tubes or filaments making up the cytoskeleton?
Microtubules, microfilaments, and intermediate filaments (MB, p. 84)

41. Microtubules are made up of the protein tubulin (MB, p. 84).

42. Microtubules function to hold organelles in place (MB, p. 84) and maintain cell shape (MB, p. 84).

43. Microfilaments are thin threadlike structures made up of the protein actin (MB, p. 84).

44. Microfilaments function primarily in cell movement (MB, p. 84).

45. Intermediate filaments function to anchor the nucleus (MB, p. 84) and maintain the shape of the nucleus (MB, p. 84).

46. Cilia and flagella are extensions of the cytoskeleton to the exterior of the cell. Both function primarily in movement (MB, p. 85).

47. Centrioles are microtubules that form when a cell is preparing to divide. What specifically do the centrioles do?
Attach to chromosomes during cell division and pull them apart (MB, p. 85)

48. List the three structures found in plant cells that are not found in animal cells and briefly state the function of each.

   a. Cell wall Function: Gives extra structure, stiffness, and protection to plant cells (MB, pp. 87-89)

   b. Plastids Function: Usually contain pigments that function in photosynthesis (MB, pp. 87-89)

   c. Water vacuole Function: Water storage (MB, pp. 87-89)

49. Which macromolecule makes up a plant cell wall? Cellulose or carbohydrate (MB, p. 88)

50. Where is the cell wall located? Outside the plasma membrane (MB, p. 88)

51. Chloroplasts like mitochondria can replicate as needed because they have their own DNA (MB, p. 89).

52. The outer and inner folded membrane of the chloroplast is made up of phospholipids (MB, p. 89).

53. The series of flattened phospholipid sacs that contain the chlorophyll is called thylakoids (MB, p. 89).

54. What is the function of the protein chlorophyll?
Traps and stores energy from sunlight (MB, p. 89)

55. Chromoplasts are organelles that contain colorful pigments, not chlorophyll (MB, p. 89).

56. These pigments may trap sunlight and participate in photosynthesis (MB, p. 89).

57. There are a variety of other types of plastids depending on the type of plant. List one other type of plastid and briefly describe its function.
Amyloplasts Function: Store starch (MB, p. 89)

CHAPTER 5: Homeostasis and Cell Transport

VOCABULARY

Section 1

1. passive transport: _____

2. diffusion: _____

3. concentration gradient: _____

4. equilibrium: _____

5. osmosis: _____

6. hypotonic: _____

7. hypertonic: _____

8. isotonic: _____

9. contractile vacuole: _____

10. turgor pressure: _____

11. plasmolysis: _____

12. cytolysis: _____

13. facilitated diffusion: _____

14. carrier protein: _____

15. ion channel: _____

SECTION REVIEW KEY

Section 1

1. Diffusion will eventually lead to a state of equilibrium in the absence of any other influence. Equilibrium is reached when the concentration of a molecule is the same throughout the space the molecule occupies. (MB, p. 97)

2. Osmosis is the passive movement of water from an area of high water concentration to an area of lower water concentration or from an area of lower solute concentration to an area of higher solute concentration. Diffusion is the movement of molecules down their own concentration gradient. (MB, pp. 97-98)

3. The solution is hypotonic to the cytosol. (MB, p. 98)

4. Carrier proteins assist the movement of non-lipid soluble molecules across the cell membrane. The molecule binds to the protein, the protein then changes its shape to shield the molecule from the hydrophobic phospholipids in the cell membrane interior, and the protein finally releases the molecule inside or outside the cell. (MB, p. 101)

5. Both are integral proteins and assist in the movement of molecules or ions across the cell membrane down their concentration or electrical gradients. Diffusion through ion channels is a type of facilitated diffusion. (MB, pp. 101-102)

6. Solutes in sea water would be hypertonic to body cells, so water would osmose out of the body cells into the extracellular fluids, causing them to shrivel or undergo plasmolysis and die. (MB, pp. 98-100)

7. A very high concentration of sugar water would again be hypertonic to the grape, so water would move out of the grape into the sugar water outside of the grape. The cells of the grape would undergo plasmolysis, shriveling and shrinking. (MB, pp. 98-100)

8. The cells of the jellyfish are nearly isotonic to sea water. Placing the jellyfish in fresh water, a hypotonic environment to the jellyfish, would cause it to take on water by osmosis. Its cells would undergo cytolysis, and it would likely swell and die. (MB, pp. 98-100)

Section 2

1. Passive transport includes processes that do not require energy as substances move down their concentration gradients. Active transport requires energy from the cell to move substances up their concentration gradients from a lower to a higher concentration. (MB, pp. 97, 103)

2. Carrier proteins act as cell membrane pumps moving specific molecules into and out of the cell against their concentration gradients. (MB, p. 103)

3. The energy to power the sodium-potassium pump is provided by the hydrolysis of one phosphate group from ATP generated by the cell's mitochondria. The liberated phosphate binds to the cell membrane pump until the sodium and potassium are passed through to the other side. (MB, pp. 103-104)

4. Pinocytosis and phagocytosis are both forms if endocytosis. Pinocytosis involves the transport of fluids and the solute in the fluids into the cell. Phagocytosis moves molecules or entire cells into the phagocytic cell. (MB, p. 105)

5. Exocytosis involves the formation of vesicles around molecules synthesized in the cell. The phospholipid membrane of the vesicle fuses with the cell membrane as its contents are released outside of the cell. (MB, p. 106)

6. Exocytosis ejects compounds from inside the cell to outside. Endocytosis brings compounds into the cell. The evidence is a change in the solute measurements both inside and outside the cell. (MB, pp. 105-106)

7. The sodium-potassium pumps embedded in the muscle cell membranes increase activity, pumping more potassium into the cell and sodium out of the cell as well as preventing any disruption of homeostasis of the organism. (MB, pp. 103-104)

8. The sodium-potassium pumps require energy to move sodium and potassium against their concentration gradients. Facilitated diffusion moves molecules down their concentration gradients and does not require energy from the cell. (MB, p. 103)

9. Fluids needed by the cell are usually moved in small quantities as to maintain a very narrow range of concentration and balance within the cell. Phagocytes may engulf large particles or even entire cells. (MB, p. 105)

Section 2

16. active transport: _____

17. sodium-potassium pump: _____

18. endocytosis: _____

19. vesicle: _____

20. pinocytosis: _____

21. phagocytosis: _____

22. phagocyte: _____

23. exocytosis: _____

COMPREHENSION QUESTIONS

Cell plasma membranes help organisms maintain homeostasis by controlling what goes into and out of the cell.

1. Types of movement of substances across a cell membrane are functionally classified into two main categories based on the energy requirement of the transfer. Substances that require no ATP for movement from the cell are classified as passive transport (MB, p. 97) while substances that require the expenditure of ATP to move across the plasma membrane are classified as active transport (MB. p. 103).

Passive Transport

2. List the three types of passive transport relative to cell metabolism and briefly explain their function.
   a. Simple diffusion Function: Primarily associated with the movement of O_2 and CO_2 (MB, pp. 97-98)
   b. Osmosis Function: The movement of water (MB, pp. 98-100)
   c. Facilitated diffusion Function: The movement of molecules through transport proteins (MB, pp. 101-102)

3. What type of energy is associated with movement and keeps atoms in constant motion? Kinetic (MB, p. 97)

4. If there is a greater amount of a substance in one area than another, a concentration gradient (MB, p. 97) is said to be present.

5. Kinetic energy will cause molecules to stay in motion constantly and be in equilibrium (MB, p. 97).

6. Molecules that pass freely through the phospholipid bilayer move down their concentration gradient by the process of simple diffusion (MB, p. 98).

7. Water moves from an area of lower solute concentration to an area of higher solute concentration by the process of osmosis (MB, p. 98).

28   Chapter 5: Homeostasis and Cell Transport

Biology Coloring Workbook

Complete Chapter 2: The Cell Membrane, Passive Transport, Active Transport and Endocytosis.

8. Molecules that are too large or repelled by the phospholipid bilayer can move down their concentration gradient by using a transport protein. This method of movement is _facilitated diffusion (MB, p. 101)_.

9. With regard to concentration gradients and cell membrane transport, label the solutions outside of the cell below and, assuming the cell membrane is permeable to the solute, label which direction the solute will move. (MB, pp. 98-99)

(a) SOLUTE
(b) WATER

WATER (OSMOSIS
vs
SOLUTE {DIFFUSION
MOVEMENT

10% salt	2% salt	30% salt
10% salt	10% salt	10% salt
Solution A	Solution B	Solution C

Type of solution? A. _Isotonic_ B. _Hypotonic_ C. _Hypertonic_

Which direction will solute move? A. _Both_ B. _Out of_ C. _Into_

10. With regard to osmosis, and the solutions/cells in the beakers above, which way will water move if the membrane is impermeable to salt and only permeable to water?

A. _Both (MB, p. 99)_ B. _Into (MB, p. 98)_ C. _Out of (MB, p. 98)_

11. Organisms such as plants or freshwater protists live in hypotonic environments and so take on osmotic water. What are two mechanisms found in these organisms that help them deal with this osmosis?

a. _Contractile vacuoles to pump osmotic water out (MB, pp. 99-100)_

b. _Solute pumps that move solute out, decreasing the concentration gradient (MB, pp. 99-100)_

12. If a cell takes on too much water or simply lacks mechanisms to eliminate osmotic water, it can burst. What is this cell bursting process called? _Cytolysis (MB, p. 100)_

And if the cell happens to be a red blood cell? _Hemolysis (IV, Ch. 5.1, Min. 29)_

13. A cell in a hypertonic environment will _lose_ water and undergo a process called _plasmolysis (MB, p. 100)_

14. The pressure osmotic water exerts on a cell wall is called _turgor (MB, p. 100)_.

15. With regard to facilitated diffusion, carrier or transport proteins carry molecules across the cell membrane down their concentration gradient. Describe in detail the process of a molecule moving through a transport protein down its concentration gradient.

The substance binds to the transport protein. The transport protein changes shape to shield the substance from the phospholipid bilayer of the cell membrane and releases it on the other side of the cell. (MB, p. 101)

Active Transport

16. What are the two distinguishing features of active transport processes?

a. _They require ATP. (MB, p. 103)_

b. _They move substances against their concentration gradients. (MB, p. 103)_

17. What are the two different types of active transport discussed?

a. _Proteins acting as cell membrane pumps (MB, pp. 104-105)_

b. _Movement in vesicles (MB, pp. 104-105)_

18. Why might cells need to pump a substance to an area where the concentration is already high?

To establish an electrical gradient that helps to start and maintain membrane permeability. This assists membranes in controlling how and when substances cross. (MB, p. 104)

19. Describe in detail the mechanism of an Na+/K+ pump.

Three sodium bind to the pump inside the cell. One molecule of ATP is cleaved into ADP, and one phosphate that stays bound to the pump. The three NA+ ions move into the pump. The protein pump shields the Na+ ions from the bilayer and releases them outside the cell. Two K+ ions bind to the pump, travel through it, and are released inside the cell. The phosphate group is released, and the process begins again. (MB, pp. 103-104)

20. How are vesicles within a cell formed?

A vesicle can be formed by the Golgi or the endoplasmic reticulum. (MB, p. 106; IV, Ch. 5.2, Min. 8-9)

21. By what process are substances in a vesicle released from a cell? Exocytosis (MB, p. 106)

22. By what process are substances taken into a cell from the extracellular fluid? Endocytosis (MB, p. 105)

23. What are the two types of endocytosis, and what type of contents are taken in with each?

a. Pinocytosis is the taking in of water and small molecules and ions in the water. (MB, p. 105)

b. Phagocytosis is the taking in of large molecules or entire cells. (MB, p. 105)

CHAPTER 8: Cellular Reproduction

VOCABULARY

Section 1

1. chromosome: _____

2. histone: _____

3. chromatid: _____

4. centromere: _____

5. chromatin: _____

6. sex chromosome: _____

7. autosome: _____

8. homologous chromosome: _____

9. karyotype: _____

10. diploid: _____

11. haploid: _____

Section 2

12. binary fission: _____

13. mitosis: _____

14. asexual reproduction: _____

15. meiosis: _____

SECTION REVIEW KEY

Section 1

1. The proteins that assist in the tight coiling of DNA into chromosomes are called histones. (MB, p. 151)

2. Prokaryotic chromosomes usually consist of a single circular molecule of DNA in the cytoplasm of the cell. Eukaryotic chromosomes are composed of nucleotides wrapped around proteins, forming multiple rod-shaped structures within the membrane-bound nucleus of the cell. (MB, pp. 151-152)

3. The number of chromosomes of any organism is not indicative of its kingdom of origin. There are some plants and animals that possess the same number of chromosomes. (MB, p. 152)

4. Each sexually reproduced organism has just one set of sex chromosomes per cell whereas there are multiple autosomes contained in each cell of the organism. (MB, p.152)

5. The diploid number of chromosomes of each organism is listed in the table. The haploid number can be calculated for each organism simply by dividing the diploid number by 2. The adder's tongue fern has a diploid number of 1,262, so its haploid gametes will have 631 chromosomes. (MB, p. 152)

6. There is no correlation. Some very simple organisms have more chromosomes than more complex organisms, and some complex organisms also have numerous chromosomes. A dog cell has 78 chromosomes and a human cell has 46. (MB, p. 152)

7. Each time a new organism was formed by sexual reproduction, it would have twice as many chromosomes as its parents, and the number would double with every subsequent generation. (MB, p. 153)

8. The individual is male since its sex chromosomes are X and Y rather than X and X. (MB, pp. 152-153)

Section 2

1. Binary fission (MB, p. 154)

2. Cytokinesis (MB, p. 155)

3. G_1 phase of interphase (MB, p. 155)

4. Anaphase (MB, p. 157)

5. Cytokinesis in animal cells begins with microtubules in the cytosol pinching the cell membrane in at the midline to form a cleavage furrow. The cleavage furrow divides the cytoplasm and its contents evenly between the two new cells. The Golgi apparatus of a plant cell forms vesicles that fuse together at the midline of the plant cell to form a cell plate. The cell plate separates the cytoplasm and will eventually become the missing cell wall of the two new cells. (MB, pp. 157-158)

6. The DNA carries the instructions for cell replication, but the timing of the replication and the advancement to the sequential phase are controlled by specific proteins in the cell. (MB, pp. 158-159)

7. There would not be an even and identical distribution of DNA between the two new cells. The newly formed cells would be mutations and likely die or be deformed and ineffective. (MB, pp. 157-158)

8. The new cells formed would receive only half of the genetic code, again resulting in mutation and likely eventual cell death and organismal death. (MB, p. 155)

9. During interphase, the DNA is loosely organized as chromatin. It is not bound into chromosomes until the cell cycle is approaching mitosis. The packing of DNA into chromosomes would make them more visible under magnification. (MB, pp. 155-156)

Section 3

1. Mitosis results in two identical diploid cells, and meiosis results in four genetically different haploid cells. (MB, p. 161)

2. With anaphase in mitosis, identical sister chromatids separate. With anaphase I of meiosis, homologous pairs separate—but not sister chromatids. (MB, pp. 157, 162)

3. The crossing-over of genes of homologues allows for endless recombination of genetic material from both parents so that potential new offspring are never identical. (MB, p. 162)

4. Telophase I (MB, p. 162)

5. Spermatogenesis produces four genetically different viable sperm cells, where oogenesis produces three small polar bodies that will later be recycled and one viable egg with most of the original cell's cytoplasm. (MB, p. 164)

6. Meiosis reduces the chromosome number of gametes to half of the original cell so that when gametes fuse during fertilization to form a new organism, the newly formed somatic cell will be diploid and different from either parent. (MB, p. 164)

7. At the end of meiosis I, sister chromatids are still joined by the centromere, and the homologues are pulled into separate cells. At the end of meiosis II, sister chromatids are pulled apart and contain only one new and different chromatid of the original cell's DNA. (MB, pp. 161-163)

8. If an error in cell division occurred during meiosis and one gamete mistakenly received 24 chromosomes rather than 23 and fertilization occurred with the mutant gamete, the resulting individual would have 47 rather than 46 chromosomes. (MB, pp. 161-163)

9. The difference in the size of the egg and sperm only has to do with the amount of cytoplasm present. An egg and sperm each carry the same amount of genetic information so when they join, the new offspring inherits equally from both parents. (MB, pp. 163-164)

16. gamete: _____

17. interphase: _____

18. cytokinesis: _____

19. prophase: _____

20. spindle fiber: _____

21. metaphase: _____

22. anaphase: _____

23. telophase: _____

24. cell plate: _____

Section 3

25. synapsis: _____

26. tetrad: _____

27. crossing-over: _____

28. genetic recombination: _____

29. independent assortment: _____

30. spermatogenesis: _____

31. oogenesis: _____

32. polar body: _____

33. sexual reproduction: _____

Biology Coloring Workbook

Complete Chapter 2: The Cell Cycle, Mitosis, Meiosis; Chapter 4: DNA and Chromosomes.

COMPREHENSION QUESTIONS

DNA and Chromosomes

1. What form does DNA take between cell divisions? Chromatin (MB, p. 152)

2. Why would DNA be in this form when a cell is not dividing?
   It is available to direct cell activities. (MB, p. 152)

3. In what form is DNA found when a cell is dividing? Chromosomes (MB, pp. 151-152)

4. What makes up a single chromosome?
   Two identical chromatids attached in the middle by a centromere (MB, p. 152)

5. What are the proteins called that help coil and pack the DNA? Histones (MB, p. 151)

6. What is the photomicrograph of an organism's genome called? Karyotype (MB, p. 153)

7. What two different types of chromosomes make up every organism's genome?
   Autosomes and sex chromosomes (MB, p. 152)

8. How many autosomes make up the human genome of every cell? 44 individual or 22 pairs (MB, p. 153)

9. What are homologous chromosomes?
   Chromosomes that are the same size and carry similar genes for the same traits. One of the
   homologues comes from the organism's mother and the other from its father. (MB, p. 152)

10. How many sex chromosomes does each cell have? Two (MB, pp. 152-153)

11. How are sex chromosomes named and what are their possible combinations?
    XX for female and XY for male (MB, pp. 152-153)

12. Every sexually reproduced organism produces two types of cells. What are these two primary cell types?
    a. Somatic cells (IV, Chapter 8.3, Minutes 14-15)
    b. Sex cells, also called gametes (eggs or sperm) (IV, Chapter 8.3, Minutes 14-15)

13. What chromosome number do somatic cells have? Diploid (MB, p. 153)

14. What is a diploid cell? A cell with homologues or a full set of chromosomes (MB, p. 153)

15. What chromosome number do sex cells have? Haploid (MB, p. 153)

16. What is a haploid cell?
    A cell with no homologues and only half the number of chromosomes the organism's somatic
    cells have (MB, p. 153)

17. If an organism has a diploid number of 84, how many chromosomes will its gametes have? 42 (MB, p. 153)

The Eukaryotic Cell Cycle: The Formation of Somatic Cells

18. Almost all cells reproduce themselves during the course of their life cycle. This series of events is called
    the cell cycle. What is the time span called between the formation of the new cell and when it begins to
    replicate again?
    Interphase (MB, p. 155)

19. Interphase is divided into three smaller phases. What are these three phases called, and what primarily occurs during each?

   a. G_1 phase: Newly formed cells mature and grow. (MB, p. 155)

   b. S phase: DNA replicates. (MB, p. 155)

   c. G_2 phase: Cell prepares to divide. (MB, p. 155)

20. During which portion of interphase do some cells exit the cell cycle? G_0 (MB, p. 155)

21. Give one example of a cell type that enters the G_0 phase. Nerve or blood cells (MB, p. 155)

22. What occurs at the end of interphase? Nuclear division or mitosis (MB, pp. 155-156)

23. What are the four shorter phases of mitosis, and what primary event(s) occur during each phase?

   a. Prophase: Nuclear envelope disintegrates and centrioles produce spindle fibers. (MB, pp. 156-157)

   b. Metaphase: Spindle fibers line the chromosomes up on the equator. (MB, pp. 156-157)

   c. Anaphase: Chromosomes are pulled apart at the centromere. (MB, pp. 156-157)

   d. Telophase: Nuclear envelopes re-form, and a cleavage furrow appears. (MB, pp. 156-157)

24. What occurs immediately following mitosis? Cytokinesis (MB, p. 157)

25. What is the end result of mitosis? Two new identical diploid cells (MB, p. 158)

26. What produces the cell wall during cytokinesis of plant cells?
   The Golgi body produces vesicles that merge into a cell plate. (MB, p. 158)

27. The centrosome and centrioles are formed from what structure? Microtubules (MB, p. 156)

Prokaryotic Cell Division

28. Prokaryotic cells reproduce by what process? Binary fission (MB, p. 154)

29. How is the DNA in prokaryotes organized? One to four circular strands (MB, p. 154)

Meiosis: Cell Division That Forms Gametes

30. What is the purpose of meiosis?
   To reduce the chromosome number and form haploid reproductive cells (MB, p. 161)

31. During what phase of the meiotic cell cycle do tetrads form? Prophase I (MB, p. 161)

32. The exchange of genetic information between a pair of homologues is called synapsis or crossing-over (MB, pp. 161-162).

33. What is the purpose of synapsis? Genetic variability (MB, pp. 161-162)

34. When are haploid cells first formed? Meiosis I (MB, pp. 161-163)

35. What is the process of the production and maturation of eggs cells called? Oogenesis (MB, p. 164)

36. What are the end products of oogenesis?
   One haploid egg and three polar bodies (MB, p. 164)

37. What is the end result of spermatogenesis?
   Four different haploid spermatocytes (MB, p. 164)

38. When human gametes join at fertilization, how many chromosomes will the resulting cell have? __46__ (MB, p. 161)

39. Label and use the circles to explain the phases and events of meiosis.

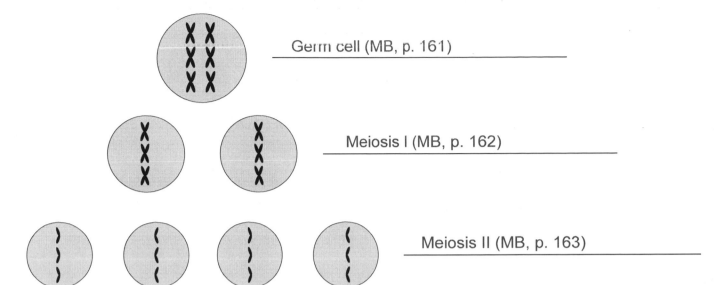

Germ cell (MB, p. 161) _____

Meiosis I (MB, p. 162) _____

Meiosis II (MB, p. 163) _____

A diploid germ cell replicates its DNA, and homologues line up on the equator; synapsis occurs where a pair of homologues exchange random sets of genes. Homologues are pulled apart to form two new haploid cells. The chromatids of these two new cells are then separated to form four new and genetically different immature gametes. (MB, pp. 161-163)

_____

_____

SECTION REVIEW KEY

Section 1

1. Live R cells did not kill the mice. Live S cells did kill the mice. Dead S cells did not kill the mice. When dead S cells (that did not kill mice) were injected with live R cells (that did not kill mice), the combination of the two did kill the mice and indicated that something in the dead S cells was passed to the live R cells to make them virulent. (MB, pp. 193-194)

2. They destroyed proteins, RNA, and DNA separately with different enzymes. Only the DNA destruction kept the dead S cells from making the live R cells virulent. The destroyed RNA and destroyed proteins had no effect on the mice. They died when the two strains were mixed. When the DNA of the dead S cells was destroyed, they did not pass on virulence. (MB, p. 194)

3. Hershey and Chase did experiments with viral DNA infecting bacteria. They were able to show that the viral DNA caused the bacteria to begin producing viruses once infected. (MB, p. 195)

4. Proteins are very heat sensitive. Once the proteins are broken down, the cell can no longer function. Bacteria are single-celled organisms. If their membrane proteins and organelles made up of protein are destroyed, they will die. (MB, pp. 193-194)

Section 2

1. X-ray diffraction photographs of DNA crystals played a key role in advancing the work of Watson and Crick. (MB, p. 196)

2. A phosphate group, a sugar (deoxyribose), and one of four different nitrogenous bases (MB, p. 197)

3. Covalent bonds hold one sugar to the adjacent phosphate group and that phosphate group to the next adjacent deoxyribose, forming the upright of the ladder or staircase. Hydrogen bonds hold complementary nitrogenous bases together, forming the rungs of the ladder or steps of the staircase. (MB, pp. 197-198)

4. Each nitrogenous base is able to bond with its complementary nitrogenous base. Adenine can only form a hydrogen bond with thymine and likewise cytosine and guanine so that one strand of DNA forms its mirror image of complementary bases on the opposite side. If one side of a DNA strand holds the nitrogenous bases CAATCG, then the opposite will hold the complement of GTTAGC. (MB, pp. 198-199)

5. Thymine forms hydrogen bonds with adenine, and guanine forms hydrogen bonds with cytosine. (MB, p. 198)

VOCABULARY

Section 1

1. virulent: _____

_____

2. transformation: _____

_____

3. bacteriophage: _____

_____

Section 2

4. nucleotide: _____

5. deoxyribose: _____

6. nitrogenous base: _____

_____

7. purine: _____

_____

8. pyrimidine: _____

9. base-pairing rules: _____

10. complementary base pair: _____

_____

11. base sequence: _____

_____

Section 3

12. DNA replication: _____

_____

13. helicase: _____

_____

14. replication fork: _____

_____

15. DNA polymerase: _____

_____

6. A single-ringed pyrimidine always forms its hydrogen bonds with a double-ringed purine, ensuring that the strands maintain their distance and consistency. (MB, p. 198)

7. 1.1 picograms, since gametes have half the number of chromosomes as somatic cells (MB, p. 155)

8. CGATTG complementary base pairs are GCTAAC. (MB, pp. 198-199)

9. 20% thymine would bond to 20% adenine, totaling 40% of the DNA and leaving 60% to account for. So cytosine and guanine would be present in equal amounts of 30%. (MB, pp. 198-199)

Section 3

1. At a replication fork in replicating DNA, the two strands separate, and complementary nucleotides are added to make two new complementary strands. (MB, p. 200)

2. The enzyme helicase breaks the hydrogen bonds between complementary nitrogenous bases, and the enzyme DNA polymerase adds complementary nucleotides to each open strand of DNA. (MB, p. 200)

3. Each new strand of DNA formed during replication holds one original strand and one newly synthesized strand. This is called semi-conservative replication. (MB, p. 200)

4. DNA replication in prokaryotes begins in one location and proceeds in opposite directions around the strand, forming two replication forks.

Section 4

16. ribonucleic acid (RNA): _____
_____

17. transcription: _____
_____

18. translation: _____
_____

19. protein synthesis: _____
_____

20. ribose: _____
_____

21. messenger RNA (mRNA): _____
_____

22. ribosomal RNA (rRNA): _____
_____

23. transfer RNA (tRNA): _____
_____

24. RNA polymerase: _____
_____

COMPREHENSION QUESTIONS

DNA Replication

1. Which scientists first visualized DNA through X-ray diffraction?
   Wilkins and Franklin (MB, pp. 196-197)

2. Which scientists developed the first model of DNA and explained how DNA replicates?
   Watson and Crick (MB, p. 196)

3. What is the monomer of DNA? How many different monomers of DNA are there?
   Nucleotide, four (MB, p. 197)

4. What three molecules compose one monomer of DNA?
   A sugar deoxyribose, a phosphate group, and a nitrogen base that is the variable (MB, p. 197)

5. What two molecules make the uprights of a DNA molecule or strand?
   The sugar and the phosphate (MB, p. 197)

6. What makes up the rungs of the DNA strand? How are all of these molecules held together?
   Two complementary nitrogen bases make up the rungs, and the two strands are held
   together by hydrogen bonds. The individual components of each strand are held together
   by covalent bonds. (MB, pp. 197-198)

DNA replication in eukaryotes begins in multiple locations along the strand and proceeds in opposite directions, forming numerous replication forks. (MB, p. 201)

5. The enzyme DNA polymerase proofs the newly formed strands of DNA and looks for any mismatched nucleotides, which it removes and replaces with the correct nucleotide. (MB, p. 202)

6. At a single replication fork, two DNA polymerases are adding nucleotides to the newly forming DNA strand. (MB, p. 200)

7. Unrepaired errors are called mutations and will have some effect on the function of the cell as well as all future replications of that cell. (MB, p. 202)

8. An early mutation of a sperm or egg cell would likely affect most of the tissues of a newly formed fetus from the mutant gamete. The outcome of a mutation of a single body cell is less critical as mutations must usually accumulate and the immune system of the body will usually eliminate mutated cells. (MB, p. 202)

Section 4

1. DNA sequences are passed to RNA, which is then passed on to the structure of proteins. (MB, p. 204)

2. The sugars in DNA and RNA are different. RNA is single stranded, RNA can leave the nucleus, RNA contains the nucleotide uracil rather than thymine, and RNA strands are usually shorter than DNA. (MB, p. 205)

3. Messenger RNA is a single stranded straight chain of nucleotides that carries the information from the nucleus to the ribosome to make specific proteins. Ribosomal RNA is a folded chain of nucleotides that makes up part of the ribosome, and transfer RNA is a single strand of RNA that is folded into a T shape and carries the code for a specific amino acid that it picks up and carries to the ribosome. (MB, p. 205)

4. RNA polymerase binds to the promoter of a gene and separates the two strands of DNA. RNA polymerase adds complementary nucleotides, forming a new strand of RNA. Once RNA polymerase reaches the termination signal on the DNA, transcription stops and the RNA molecule leaves the nucleus. (MB, p. 206)

5. The genetic code is the sequences of nucleotides on mRNA and how they translate into amino acids laid down sequentially for the synthesis of a specific protein. (MB, p. 207)

6. mRNA carries the codes for protein synthesis from the nucleus to the ribosome in the cytosol. The rRNA forms the ribosome and acts as a binding site for the mRNA, while tRNA carries the amino acids to their binding site on the growing polypeptide. (MB, pp. 208-209)

7. Knowing which DNA sequences code for specific functions and characteristics assists researchers and doctors with diagnosing and treating genetic disorders and mutations forming cancer. (MB, p. 210)

8. RNA polymerase catalyzes the formation of RNA, while DNA polymerase catalyzes the formation of DNA. (MB, p. 206)

9. UAA is a stop codon, so no amino acids would form a peptide in this case. (MB, p. 207)

10. The two strands of a DNA double helix are different. The RNA strands that form from each side would also be different and so would the proteins formed from those different codes. (MB, p. 206)

11. tRNA carries the anticodon that is complementary to the codon on the mRNA. tRNA also carries the amino acid that is coded for at the opposite end of its anticodon. (MB, pp. 208-209)

Biology Coloring Workbook

Complete Chapter 4: Eukaryotic DNA Replication, Replication of DNA, Protein Synthesis (Transcription), Protein Synthesis (Translation).

7. Into what two groups are the nitrogen bases divided? What is this classification based on? Which bases are in each group?

     The two classification groups for nitrogen bases are purines and pyrimidines. Purines are double carbon ring structures, while pyrimidines are single carbon ring structures. The purines include adenine and guanine, and the pyrimidines are thymine and cytosine. (MB, p. 198)

8. Which nitrogen bases form bonds with each other? (Follow base-pairing rules.)

     Guanine always forms three hydrogen bonds only with cytosine. Adenine forms two hydrogen bonds only with thymine. (MB, p. 198)

9. What are the three enzymes that participate in DNA replication, and what are their functions?

     DNA helicase breaks the hydrogen bonds between the nitrogen bases, separating the strand. DNA polymerase adds new nucleotides to form two new strands and proofs any errors. DNA ligase joins the gaps in the strands. (MB, pp. 200-201)

10. Explain semi-conservative replication.

     Each new DNA strand has one original strand and a newly made strand to make two new double-stranded helices. (MB, p. 200)

11. Explain the direction and action of the replication forks.

     DNA helicase forms the replication forks at multiple sites along the DNA strand. DNA polymerase then adds nucleotides in opposite directions on both sides of the double helix at each replication fork. (MB, pp. 200-201)

12. Is DNA replication accurate, and which enzyme proofs and removes faulty pairings?

     DNA replication is very accurate, and DNA polymerase repairs any errors in replication. (MB, p. 202)

13. What is a mutation? What are the possible results of a mutation?

     A mutation occurs any time a nucleotide remains that differs from the original parent strand. Some mutations can be fatal and lead to cancer or abnormalities in form or function. Some mutations may improve the organism and are the basis for the theory of evolution. (MB, p. 200)

Protein Synthesis

14. What is a gene?

A segment of DNA that codes for a specific trait or function (MB, p. 204)

15. What are the two different steps of protein synthesis?

Transcription and translation (MB, p. 204)

16. What is the monomer of RNA? How many different monomers are there?

Nucleotide, four (MB, p. 205)

17. What three molecules make up a monomer of RNA?

The sugar ribose, a phosphate, and a nitrogen base (MB, p. 205)

18. What are the three major forms of RNA? What is the primary function of each?

a. Messenger RNA (mRNA) Forms a template from DNA that codes for a protein (MB, p. 205)

b. Ribosomal RNA (rRNA)   Makes up part of the ribosome (MB, p. 205)

c. Transfer RNA (tRNA) Carries the amino acid to the ribosome and places it in position (MB, p. 205)

19. What are the major differences between DNA and RNA?

a. DNA is double stranded; RNA is single stranded (MB, p. 205)

b. DNA strands are longer than RNA (MB, p. 205)

c. DNA contains the nitrogen base thymine; RNA uses uracil in place of thymine (MB, p. 205)

20. What is the end product of transcription?

A strand of mRNA (MB, p. 206)

21. What is the promoter? A base triplet? A termination signal?

The promoter is a segment of DNA that signals the beginning of transcription. A base triplet is a series of three nucleotides that code for a specific amino acid. The termination signal is a series of nucleotides on the DNA that signals the end of transcription. (MB, p. 206)

22. What are codons? Where are they found?

A codon is a series of three nucleotides on the mRNA that code for a specific amino acid. (MB, p. 207)

23. What are the start and stop codons? Do they code for a specific amino acid?

There is one start codon AUG that codes for the amino acid methionine. There are several different stop codons that do not code for any amino acid. (MB, p. 207)

24. What enzyme catalyzes the formation of RNA from DNA?

RNA polymerase (MB, p. 206)

25. Do some amino acids have more than one codon?

Most amino acids have several different codons. (MB, p. 207)

26. What are the four main steps of translation? What occurs during each step?

a. ___Initiation: mRNA attaches to a ribosome and the tRNA carrying methionine docks on___ ___the mRNA. (MB, pp. 208-209)___

b. ___Elongation: tRNA brings amino acids and the polypeptide is assembled according to___ ___the codons. (MB, pp. 208-209)___

c. ___Termination: The stop codon is reached on the ribosome and the polypeptide___ ___is completed. (MB, pp. 208-209)___

d. ___Disassembly: All elements of translation are broken down and recycled. (MB, pp. 208-209)___

27. What type of bond is formed between adjacent amino acids?

Peptide (MB, p. 207)

28. Where do transcription and translation take place in prokaryotes?

Both in the cytoplasm (MB, pp. 206, 208)

29. Which types of cells make proteins?

All cells produce protein specific to the cell. (IV, Chapter 10.4, Minute 2)

30. Approximately how many genes make up the human genome? Approximately how many base pairs make up those genes?

30,000 genes and 3.2 billion base pairs (MB, p. 210)

PROTEIN SYNTHESIS DIAGRAM
Complete the following on the diagram below.

- ☐ Color the DNA backbones blue.
- ☐ Color the mRNA backbones green.
- ☐ Color the tRNA yellow.
- ☐ Color the amino acids red.
- ☐ Fill in the complementary nucleotides on the unlabeled DNA strand.
  (MB, pp. 206, 209)

- ☐ Fill in the complementary nucleotides on the mRNA strand adjacent to the DNA strands.
- ☐ Translate these same nucleotides to the mRNA strand where it docks on the ribosome.
- ☐ Fill in the anticodons on the tRNA molecules according to the codons on the mRNA.

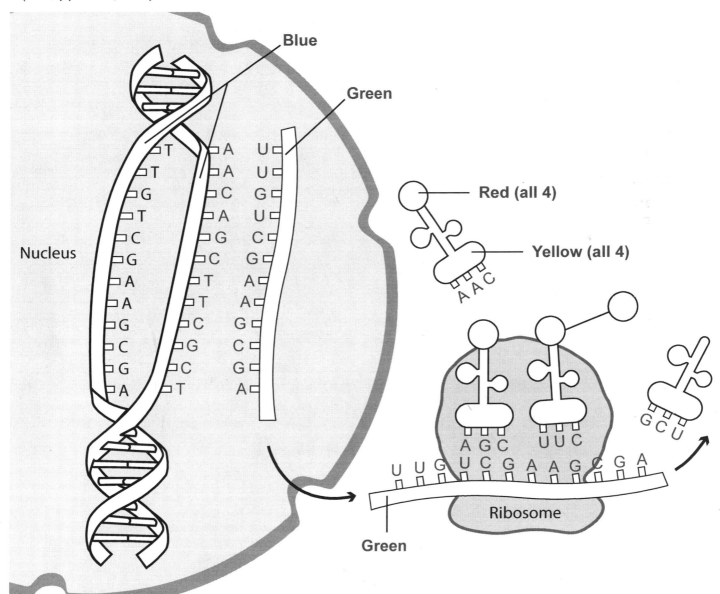

Answer the following questions.

31. What is the sequence of three nucleotides on the mRNA called? _____Codon (MB, p. 207)_____

32. What is the sequence of three nucleotides on the tRNA called? _____Anticodon (MB, p. 208)_____

33. What is the sequence of three nucleotides on a DNA strand called? _Base triplet (IV, Ch. 10.4, Min. 18)_

SECOND TRIMESTER

SECTION REVIEW KEY

Section 1

1. True-breeding plants are plants that consistently produce offspring with a specific trait for which they are bred whenever they self-pollinate. Any genetic factors for the contrasting trait have been eliminated by repeated self-pollination. (MB, p. 175)

2. Mendel produced true-breeding plants for two contrasting factors of a trait. He then cross-pollinated the two true-breeders to produce an F_1 generation of plants that would have carried both factors for the trait. (MB, p. 175)

3. A dominant factor, when crossed with a recessive factor, masks the expression of the recessive factor or allele. When a dominant allele and a recessive allele are both present in the genome of an organism, the recessive allele has no visible expression in the organism. (MB, p. 177)

4. The law of segregation states that paired alleles are separated during meiosis. The law of independent assortment states that alleles separate independent of one another as long as they are located on different chromosomes or far apart on the same chromosome. (MB, pp. 177-178)

5. A gene is a segment of a chromosome that codes for a specific cellular function or a hereditary trait. An allele is one of two or more alternative forms of a gene. (MB, p. 178)

6. The F_1 plants had been cross-pollinated from two true-breeding plants, one with the dominant allele and one with the recessive allele. The F_1 offspring all exhibited the dominant trait. The F_2 generation was the offspring of self-pollinated F_1 generation plants, and they exhibited both the dominant and recessive trait in a 3:1 ratio. (MB, pp. 175-177)

7. The disorder must be recessive, and each parent must carry both a dominant and a recessive allele for the disorder. In order for the offspring to exhibit the trait, the child must receive the recessive gene from each parent. (MB, pp. 173, 177)

8. Crossing-over during prophase I of meiosis allows for the independent separation of genes making up the chromosomes. (MB, p. 161)

Section 2

1. Both homozygous dominant and heterozygous genotypes have the same

---

VOCABULARY

Section 1

1. genetics: _____

2. heredity: _____

3. trait: _____

4. pollination: _____

5. self-pollination: _____

6. cross-pollination: _____

7. true-breeding: _____

8. P generation: _____

9. F_1 generation: _____

10. F_2 generation: _____

11. dominant: _____

12. recessive: _____

13. law of segregation: _____

14. law of independent assortment: _____

15. molecular genetics: _____

16. allele: _____

---

phenotype. Some external environmental factors may also affect the phenotype. (MB, pp. 180-181)

2. Probability is equal to the number of times something is expected to happen divided by the number of times it could happen. (MB, p. 181)

3. The purple-flowering plant, which we assume is the dominant trait, can be crossed with a homozygous recessive plant. If any of the recessive trait shows up in the offspring of the cross, the purple-flowering plant must be heterozygous for the trait of flower color. (MB, p. 182)

4. The Punnett square should have the genotype of each parent alongside the top and left side of the grid, and each possible allele combination should be demonstrated. (MB, pp. 182-183)

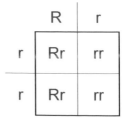

	R	r
r	Rr	rr
r	Rr	rr

Section 2

17. genotype: _____
_____

18. phenotype: _____
_____

19. homozygous: _____
_____

20. heterozygous: _____
_____

21. probability: _____
_____

22. monohybrid cross: _____
_____

23. Punnett square: _____
_____

24. genotypic ratio: _____
_____

25. phenotypic ratio: _____
_____

26. testcross: _____
_____

27. complete dominance: _____
_____

28. incomplete dominance: _____
_____

29. codominance: _____
_____

30. dihybrid cross: _____
_____

COMPREHENSION QUESTIONS

Assume complete dominance unless otherwise stated.

1. What is the genotype for an organism that is heterozygous for green fur color? __Gg (MB, p. 181)__

2. True-breeders are also called __P generation (MB, p. 175)__ .

3. An organism that has inherited two of the same alleles of a gene from both parents is considered __homozygous (MB, p. 181)__ for that trait.

4. A monohybrid cross tracks a __single (MB, p. 182)__ characteristic.

5. A monohybrid cross is a cross in which only one trait is tracked, such as flower color. A dihybrid cross simultaneously tracks two different traits, such as flower color and seed color or plant height along with leaf position. (MB, pp. 182, 185)

6. The trait for tail length must exhibit incomplete dominance in order for two parents both with short tails to produce offspring with three different phenotypes. The parents both had short tails rather than no tail or a long tail, so their genotypes had to be both heterozygous for tail length. (MB, pp. 180-181)

7. At least one or both parents were homozygous dominant for flower color for all offspring to exhibit the purple phenotype. If the recessive trait is exhibited at all in an F_1 generation, both parents had to be heterozygous. (MB, p. 181)

Biology Coloring Workbook

Complete Chapter 3: The Monohybrid Cross, The Dihybrid Cross, The Testcross, Incomplete Dominance.

5. Give an example of a homozygous genotype. BB or bb (MB, pp. 181-182) (choose any letter)

6. In a monohybrid cross between a homozygous dominant parent and a homozygous recessive parent, what would you predict the genotypic ratio of offspring to be? 4:0 all heterozygous (MB, p. 181)

7. In a monohybrid cross between two heterozygous parents, what would you expect the phenotypic ratio of the offspring to be? 1:2 (MB, p. 181)

8. In hamsters, brown fur is dominant. A brown hamster is crossed with a white albino hamster. If the litter contains a white offspring, the genotype of the brown-haired parent is probably Bb or heterozygous (MB, p. 182)

9. To determine the genotype of an individual that exhibits the dominant phenotype, you would cross that individual with one that is homozygous recessive for that trait (MB, pp. 182-183).

10. If two parents with dominant phenotypes produce an offspring with a recessive phenotype, then most likely the parents are both heterozygous (MB, pp. 182-183)

11. A trait occurring in 600 offspring out of a total of 1,200 offspring has a probability of 50% (MB, p. 181).

12. Suppose you have discovered a new species of beetle. Some of the beetles have yellow spots and some have red spots. You cross a red spotted beetle with a yellow spotted beetle and all of the resulting offspring have orange spots. What is the most likely genotype of the offspring? Rr or Yy (MB, pp. 180-181)

13. What was Gregor Mendel's occupation, training, and nationality?
He was an Austrian monk gardener who studied statistics in university. (MB, p. 173)

14. Write the probability equation:
the number of times an event occurs / the number of times the event could have occurred (MB, p. 181)

15. Two alternative forms of a gene are called alleles (MB, p. 178).

16. A gene is a segment of DNA that codes for a specific trait or cell function (MB, p. 9).

17. Phenotype is the physical manifestation or appearance of a gene (MB, p. 180).

18. Genotype is the specific alleles that produce a trait (MB, p. 180).

19. Heredity is alleles passed from one generation to another (MB, p. 173).

20. The law of independent assortment says that traits sort independently of each other unless they are adjacent on a chromosome (MB, pp. 177-178).

21. The law of segregation states that during meiosis, each newly formed gamete receives a full yet unique complement of both parents' genomes (MB, p. 177)

22. Describe Mendel's experiments on pea plants. Make sure you include all of the generations and the steps he took as he completed his experiments as well as his results.

1. Mendel produced true-breeding plants for each trait of all seven characteristics by self-pollinating each one until he no longer reproduced any trait except the one he was breeding for. He produced fourteen true-breeding plants that he called his P generation.

2. He then cross-pollinated the two true-breeding traits for each characteristic—for example, a true-breeding white pea plant with a true-breeding purple pea plant. This resulted in offspring that only exhibited one of the colors; in this example, they were all purple. He concluded that one trait was dominant over the other. He called these his F_1 generation.

3. He then self-pollinated each of his F_1 generation plants, which resulted in a 3:1 ratio of traits, three purple and one white. He called these his F_2 generation. He concluded there were a pair of factors controlling the expression of the trait, one coming from each parent; in the presence of the dominant factor, the recessive factor would not be expressed. (MB, pp. 173-178)

23. Yellow flowers are completely dominant in daffodils. How can you determine the genotype of a yellow-flowering daffodil? Draw Punnett squares to demonstrate.

Perform a testcross (cross the dominant phenotype with a homozygous recessive phenotype) to determine the genotype of a dominant phenotype. If there are any offspring exhibiting the recessive trait, the unknown genotype would have to be heterozygous.   YY   Yy

(MB, pp. 182-184)

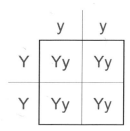
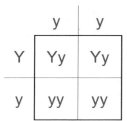

24. Complete the Punnett square with two heterozygous parents. Think up your own two traits.

Mom = TtSs

	TS	Ts	tS	ts
TS	TTSS	TTSs	TtSS	TtSs
Ts	TTSs	TTss	TtSs	Ttss
tS	TtSS	TtSs	ttSS	ttSs
ts	TtSs	Ttss	ttSs	ttss

Dad = TtSs

Traits: ___Tall and Skinny___ vs. ___short and stocky___

Genotypes: ___TtSS___

(MB, pp. 182-183)

a. List all possible genotypes and the number occurring of each.

TTSS-1, TtSS-2, TTSs-2, TtSs-4, TTss-1, Ttss-2, ttSS-1, ttSs-2, ttss-1 = 16 Total (MB, pp. 185-186)

b. What is the genotype ratio of the offspring?

1:2:2:4:1:2:1:2:1 (MB, p. 183)

c. What are the possible phenotypes and the genotypes associated with that phenotype?

Tall and Skinny: TTSS, TTSs, TtSS, TtSs	Total Tall and Skinny = 9
Tall and stocky: TTss, Ttss	Total Tall and stocky = 3
short and Skinny: ttSS, ttSs	Total short and Skinny = 3
short and stocky: ttss	Total short and stocky = 1 (MB, pp. 182-183)

d. What is the phenotype ratio of the offspring?

9:3:3:1 (MB, p. 183)

e. What are the genotypes of the two parents?

They are both heterozygous for both traits: TtSs (MB, pp. 181, 183)

CHAPTER 23: Bacteria

VOCABULARY

Section 1

1. prokaryote: _____

2. peptidoglycan: _____

3. methanogen: _____

4. halophile: _____

5. thermoacidophile: _____

6. bacillus: _____

7. coccus: _____

8. spirillum: _____

9. streptococcus: _____

10. staphylococcus: _____

11. Gram-negative bacterium: _____

12. Gram-positive bacterium: _____

13. antibiotic: _____

Section 2

14. plasmid: _____

15. capsule: _____

16. glycocalyx: _____

SECTION REVIEW KEY

Section 1

1. Archaea lack a membrane-bound nucleus, making them more like bacteria and unlike eukaryotes. But much like eukaryotes, they have no peptidoglycan in their cell membranes, and they have introns located in their DNA. (MB, p. 462)

2. Hot, acidic environments such as volcanic or thermal vents, high salt environments such as the Dead Sea and the Great Salt Lake, and anaerobic environments such as intestines and swamps (MB, p. 462)

3. Gram staining helps classify bacteria into two groups based on the amount of peptidoglycan in the cell membrane of the microbes. They stain purple or pink, classifying them as Gram-positive or Gram-negative. (MB, p. 463)

4. Proteobacteria: Rhizobium or Helicobacter pylori
   Gram-positive: Clostridium botulinum, Bacillus anthracis, or actinomycetes
   Cyanobacteria: Anabaena

Spirochetes: Treponema pallidum, Borelia burgdorferi
Chlamydia: Chlamydia trachomatis (MB, pp. 464-466)

5. Nitrogen-fixing bacteria are bacteria that inhabit the soil and roots of certain plants that have the ability to convert atmospheric nitrogen into a form the plants can use as nutrition. (MB, pp. 464-465)

6. It is thought that cyanobacteria were the first oxygen-producing bacteria contributing to the formation of an oxygen-rich atmosphere and the formation of ozone, which would have made it possible for other aerobic organisms to develop. (MB, p. 466)

7. Chemoautotrophs or anything nonphotosynthetic (MB, p. 462)

8. No. Thermoacidophiles live in the hottest, most acidic environments on Earth. Enteric bacteria could not live in these very harsh environments. (MB, pp. 462, 465)

9. An antibiotic should only be used if the microbe has been identified as either Gram-positive or Gram-negative, and the antibiotic used should be specific to the microbe. (MB, p. 465)

Section 2

1. Any reasonable answers. See Table 23-1.
   Capsule: protection
   Cell wall: protection and shape
   Cell membrane: controls what goes into and out of the cell
   Cytoplasm: holds the cell contents
   Chromosome: controls cell activity and stores hereditary information
   Plasmids: carry genes for transfer
   Endospore: allows bacteria to regenerate when conditions are favorable
   Pilus: used for attaching to other cells or surfaces and functions in conjugation
   Flagella: locomotion (MB, pp. 467-468)

2. Flagella, cytoplasmic streaming, and spirochete rotation (MB, p. 469)

3. Some prokaryotes cannot survive in the presence of oxygen and are called obligate anaerobes. Some prokaryotes can tolerate an oxygen-rich or oxygen-absent environment and are called facultative anaerobes. Those prokaryotes that need oxygen to survive are called obligate aerobes. (MB, p. 470)

4. Autotrophs obtain carbon from carbon dioxide, and heterotrophs obtain carbon from other organisms. (MB, p. 469)

5. Transformation: Bacteria obtain DNA from somewhere in their external environment and incorporate that DNA into their own genome.

   Transduction: A virus transfers DNA fragments from one bacteria to another.

   Conjugation: One prokaryote transfers its genome directly to another through a pilus. (MB, p. 471)

6. Chloroplasts (MB, p. 467)

7. The endospore would be able to germinate in the anaerobic environment of the can. (MB, p. 470)

8. No new organism is formed in recombination. There is simply a sharing and reorganization of DNA. (MB, p. 471)

SECTION 3

1. Bacteria either produce toxins or they secrete digestive enzymes that destroy tissues. (MB, p. 472)

2. Antibiotics compete for resources. (MB, p. 473)

3. When bacteria survive an exposure to antibiotics and gain useful information that helps them to resist the antibiotic, they become a resistant population of microbes. (MB, p. 473)

4. Some diseases can no longer be treated with antibiotics that used to be effective treatments. (MB, p. 473)

5. By cooking and proper food handling (MB, p. 474)

6. Some bacteria are able to use the pollutants as an energy source and so when applied, can consume the pollutant, leaving harmless chemicals as a waste by-product. (MB, p. 476)

7. Since resistant bacteria are the ones that live, they are able to pass the resistance on to offspring, making them resistant (microevolution of the species). (MB, p. 473)

8. Fermentation is an anaerobic process. Pickles are fermented cucumbers. (MB, p. 470)

9. No. Some very healthy foods can only form from the action of bacteria on the food. Also, not all bacteria cause disease; some are benign. (MB, p. 476)

17. pilus: _____

18. endospore: _____

19. heterotroph: _____

20. autotroph: _____

21. phototroph: _____

22. chemotroph: _____

23. obligate anaerobe: _____

24. facultative anaerobe: _____

25. obligate aerobe: _____

26. transformation: _____

27. conjugation: _____

28. transduction: _____

Section 3

29. pathology: _____

30. exotoxin: _____

31. endotoxin: _____

32. antibiotic resistance: _____

33. zoonosis: _____

34. bioremediation: _____

Biology Coloring Workbook

Complete Chapter 6: Bacteria.

COMPREHENSION QUESTIONS

1. What primary feature distinguishes prokaryotes from eukaryotes?
   Prokaryotes have no membrane-bound nucleus or membrane-bound organelles. (MB, p. 461)

2. What is the most common body morphology of prokaryotes? _____Unicellular (MB, p. 461)_____

3. Where are prokaryotes found? _____Everywhere (MB, p. 461)_____

4. What are the two domains of prokaryotes? _____Archaea and bacteria (MB, p. 461)_____

5. What four features distinguish archaea from bacteria?
   a. rRNA more closely resembles eukaryotic cells than bacterial cells. (MB, p. 461)
   b. The cell wall of archaea has no molecules called peptidoglycan. (MB, p. 462)
   c. The cell membrane lipids of archaea are different from bacteria. (MB, p. 462)
   d. DNA of archaea include introns (untranslated segments of DNA) unlike bacteria. (MB, p. 462)

6. What are the three primary groups of archaea?
   a. _____Methanogens (MB, p. 462)_____
   b. _____Halogens (MB, p. 462)_____
   c. _____Thermoacidophiles (MB, p. 462)_____

7. In what unique way do methanogens acquire energy?
   They convert hydrogen gas and carbon dioxide into methane gas. (MB, p. 462)

8. Where would you most likely find a methanogen?
   They are anaerobic so they would be found where there is little to no oxygen: intestines,
   swamp mud, sewage, deep water, or marine mud. (MB, p. 462)

9. Halophiles have an affinity for what compound? _____Salt (MB, p. 462)_____

10. Where would you most likely find a halophile? _____Great Salt Lake or Dead Sea (MB, p. 462)_____

11. Where would you most likely find a thermoacidophile?
    Hot acidic environments such as hot springs, volcanic vents, and hydrothermal vents. (MB, p. 462)

12. How are thermoacidophiles ecologically important?
    They are an important source of food for deep water clams, crabs, and mussels. (MB, p. 462)

13. List four criteria used as a basis for classifying bacteria.
    a. _____Shape (MB, pp. 463-464)_____
    b. _____Staining capability (MB, pp. 463-464)_____
    c. _____Biochemical features (MB, pp. 463-464)_____
    d. _____Evolutionary properties (MB, pp. 463-464)_____

14. What are the three primary shapes of bacteria and their proper names? (Fig. 23-3 in the text.)

   a.   Bacillus: rod-shaped (MB, p. 463)

   b.   Coccus: sphere-shaped (MB, p. 463)

   c.   Spirillum: spiral-shaped (MB, p. 463)

15. How are streptococcus and staphylococcus different?

Streptococcus is cocci in chains, while staphylococcus grows in clusters. (MB, p. 463)

16. What are the three Gram stain classifications?

   a. Gram-negative bacteria stain pink due to small amounts of peptidoglycan (IV, Ch. 23.1, Min. 20-21)

   b. Gram-positive bacteria stain purple due to large amounts of peptidoglycan (IV, Ch. 23.1, Min. 20-21)

   c. Gram-variable bacteria stain purple and pink due to their mixed nature (IV, Ch. 23.1, Min. 20-21)

17. What are the four primary steps for Gram staining bacteria?

   a.   Crystal violet stains the bacteria. (IV, Ch. 23.1, Min. 22-24)

   b.   Iodine traps the crystal violet to form a CV-I complex. (IV, Ch. 23.1, Min. 22-24)

   c.   Alcohol or acetone washes away unstained cell wall. (IV, Ch. 23.1, Min. 22-24)

   d.   Safranin counterstains the Gram-negative cells pink. (IV, Ch. 23.1, Min. 22-24)

18. Why do some bacteria stain different colors?

The compound peptidoglycan in the cell wall picks up the crystal violet and is stained. Gram-positive bacteria have a large amount of peptidoglycan and so stain deep purple. Gram-negative bacteria have very little peptidoglycan and so do not pick up the stain. (IV, Ch. 23.1, Min. 20) (MB, p. 463)

19. Why are nitrogen-fixing bacteria important?

They convert atmospheric nitrogen into usable soil nitrogen for plants. (MB, p. 465)

20. Why are cyanobacteria important?

They are photosynthetic bacteria and so produce much oxygen for other organisms. They are also thought to be Earth's first oxygen producers. (MB, p. 466)

21. Where does photosynthesis take place in cyanobacteria?

Thylakoids embedded in the plasma membrane (MB, p. 467)

22. List the structures you would most likely find in/on a bacterial cell, and briefly explain the function of each structure.

   a. Plasma membrane: Phospholipid bilayer controls what goes into and out of the cell. (MB, p. 467)

   b. Cell wall: Gives the cell protection and support (MB, p. 467)

   c. Capsule: Found in some bacteria; aids in resistance and pathogenesis (MB, p. 468)

   d. Nucleoid or DNA: Genome that controls cell activities (MB, p. 468)

   e. Ribosomes: Provide a site for protein synthesis (MB, p. 468)

   f. Plasmids: Loops of resistant DNA to be passed to other bacteria (MB, p. 468)

   g. Endospore: Encapsulated DNA that allows some bacteria to regenerate if conditions are favorable (MB, pp. 468-469)

   h. Flagella: Whiplike filaments used for locomotion (MB, pp. 468-469)

   i. Pilus: Microtubule that allows bacteria to stick and conjugate (MB, p. 468)

   j. Glycocalyx: Sticky sugar coating on the capsule, which helps bacteria adhere to tissues and other bacteria (MB, p. 468)

23. Where does cell respiration occur in prokaryotes?
   Proteins embedded in the plasma membrane (MB, p. 467)

24. What are the primary means of locomotion by bacteria?
   Flagella, slime movement, or corkscrew rotation (MB, p. 469)

25. What are the four nutritional groups of bacteria, and how does each obtain carbon and energy?

   a. Photoautotrophs: Energy from the sun, carbon from CO_2 (MB, p. 469)

   b. Chemoautotrophs: Energy from compounds, carbon from CO_2 (MB, p. 469)

   c. Photoheterotrophs: Energy from sun, carbon from other organisms (MB, p. 469)

   d. Chemoheterotrophs: Energy from compounds, carbon from other organisms (MB, p. 469)

26. What three factors determine the habitat of bacteria? Oxygen needs, pH, temperature (MB, p. 470)

27. What are the three different oxygen classifications of bacteria?

   a. Obligate aerobes must have oxygen. (MB, p. 470)

   b. Obligate anaerobes cannot live in the presence of oxygen. (MB, p. 470)

   c. Facultative anaerobes can live in or out of oxygen. (MB, p. 470)

28. What pH is preferred by most bacteria? Neutral pH, 6.5-7.5 (MB, p. 470)

29. What are the three different temperature classifications of bacteria?

   a. Psychrophilic: Prefer cold temperatures (MB, p. 470)

   b. Mesophilic: Prefer moderate temperatures (MB, p. 470)

   c. Thermophilic: Prefer hot temperatures (MB, p. 470)

30. How do bacteria reproduce? Binary fission (MB, p. 471)

31. Briefly explain the three processes bacteria utilize to mutate and recombine DNA?

a. Conjugation: DNA is passed from one bacteria to another through a plasmid. (MB, p. 471)

b. Transformation: DNA is taken in from the bacteria's environment. (MB, p. 471)

c. Transduction: A virus infects a bacteria, inserting its DNA into the bacterial genome. (MB, p. 471)

32. How do pathogenic bacteria cause disease?

They produce toxins or break down host tissues by secreting digestive enzymes that destroy host tissues. (MB, pp. 472-473)

33. How do antibiotics destroy bacteria?

They either block the production of new cell wall or they block protein synthesis. (MB, p. 473)

34. How do pathogenic bacteria become antibiotic resistant?

They acquire a plasmid through conjugation from another bacteria that carries resistant DNA. (MB, p. 473)

35. What type of bacteria would you most likely find in the human intestine? Enteric (MB, p. 465)

36. Which bacteria causes the most cases of food poisoning in the U.S.? How is this same bacteria beneficial?

Escherichia coli; specific strains help with the formation of vitamin K in the intestine (MB, p. 465)

37. Which bacteria causes stomach ulcers? Helicobacter pylori (MB, p. 465)

38. How is the bacteria Clostridium botulinum used by doctors? Botox to remove skin wrinkles (MB, p. 465)

39. If ingested, what are the effects of c. Botulinum? Severe intestinal illness and possibly death (MB, p. 465)

40. What is the habitat of actinomycetes and how are they used pharmaceutically?

Actinomycetes are bacteria that live in soil and are used to make several different antibiotics. (MB, p. 465)

41. Which group of bacteria causes both TB and leprosy? Mycobacteria (MB, p. 474)

42. Which bacteria causes Lyme disease, and how is it transmitted?

Borelia burgdorferi is transmitted through tick bites. (MB, p. 474)

43. Who first visualized living bacteria and when? Anton van Leeuwenhoek in 1677 (MB, p. 475)

44. Who was the first scientist to discover that heat kills most bacteria and institute sterilization technique?

Louis Pasteur (MB, p. 475)

45. Who was the scientist to discover the antibiotic properties of penicillin? Alexander Fleming (MB, p. 475)

46. The process of using bacterial growth to break down pollutants is called bioremediation (MB, p. 476).

47. How are bacteria used to genetically modify food?

Specific bacterial genes are inserted into the genome of some plants to make them pest resistant. bioremediation (MB, p. 476)

48. List several common foods that are produced by the action of bacteria.

Yogurt, soy sauce, pickles, etc. bioremediation (MB, p. 476)

CHAPTER 24: Viruses

VOCABULARY

Section 1

1. virus: _____

2. capsid: _____

3. envelope: _____

4. provirus: _____

5. retrovirus: _____

6. reverse transcriptase: _____

7. bacteriophage: _____

8. lytic cycle: _____

9. virulent: _____

10. lysis: _____

11. lysogenic cycle: _____

12. temperate virus: _____

13. prophage: _____

Section 2

14. vector: _____

15. protease inhibitor: _____

16. oncogene: _____

SECTION REVIEW KEY

Section 1

1. The virus was crystallized, indicating that it was not composed of cells. (MB, p. 483)

2. Viruses do not exhibit any of the seven properties of life. (MB, p. 483)

3. Bacteriophages have a complex capsid with a hexagonal head filled with DNA. Attached to the head by a collar is a protein tail with multiple tail fibers. (MB, p. 486)

4. During a viral lytic cycle, the virus gains access to a cell and takes over the mechanics to produce new viruses; then the cell bursts, releasing the newly made viruses. During the lysogenic cycle, once the virus gains access to the cell, it integrates its genome into the host genome and then may lie dormant for long periods before it may enter the lytic cycle and begin producing more viruses. (MB, pp. 486–487)

5. It is thought that early viruses were likely naked pieces of nucleic acid, either RNA or DNA that inadvertently entered a cell through a damaged cell membrane and the cell incorporated the nucleic acid into its own genome. (MB, p. 488)

6. Genetic material, either DNA or RNA, does not constitute life on its own. A virus without a host cell cannot replicate, does not exhibit metabolism, has no homeostasis to maintain, is not made up of cells, and cannot respond to stimuli. It has no properties of life on its own. (MB, p. 483)

7. Bacteria are prokaryotic cells and so have no membrane-bound nucleus. Bacteriophage are viruses that only infect bacteria. (MB, p. 486)

8. Most colds are caused by viruses, and antibiotics have no ability to destroy viruses or cells infected by viruses. (MB, p. 475)

Section 2

1. Infected animals are vectors for rabies, mosquitoes are vectors for West Nile virus, and SARS virus is transferred by an infected species of cat. (MB, p. 489)

2. HIV, Ebola, herpes, HPV, hepatitis (MB, pp. 489-491)

3. Some viruses have genes that control cell growth and/or replication. These are called oncogenes. If a virus inserts an oncogene into the host gene, it can lead to tumor growth. Other viruses may cause certain host genes to become oncogenes. (MB, p. 491)

4. As humans move into and consume previously uninhabited lands, they come in contact with animals that have not had previous human contact. These animals may be infected with viruses that humans have not previously been exposed to. (MB, p. 491)

5. Vector control, vaccinations, and antiviral drugs. (MB, p. 492)

6. Viruses and viroids both have nucleic acids. While a viroid is a naked piece of nucleic acid, a virus has a capsid to house its nucleic acid. Prions are naked protein particles that are capable of causing disease. (MB, p. 494)

7. No. An emerging virus is a virus that has existed but has not previously infected human hosts. (MB, p. 491)

8. Antibiotics are not effective in treating viral infections. Every time an antibiotic is used, it gives bacteria and other disease-causing microbes, not viruses, the opportunity to mutate and become antibiotic resistant. (MB, p. 473)

9. It allows them to recognize and be recognized by more types of receptor proteins, gaining access to more types of cells. (MB, pp. 490-491)

Biology Coloring Workbook

Complete Chapter 6: Viruses.

17. **proto-oncogene:**_____

_____

18. **emerging disease:**_____

_____

19. **viroid:**_____

_____

20. **prion:**_____

_____

COMPREHENSION QUESTIONS

1. Who was the first scientist to crystallize a virus? What virus was it?
   Wendell Stanley crystallized tobacco mosaic virus (TMV). (MB, p. 483)

2. What are the physical structures making up a virus?
   A typical virus is made up of a capsid and a genome, either RNA or DNA. Some viruses have
   envelopes built from host cell materials. (MB, p. 484)

3. What determines the shape of the capsid?
   The type of genome making up the virus (MB, p. 484)

4. What are the three primary capsid shapes? Spherical, helical, and icosahedral (MB, p. 484)

5. Give an example of a disease associated with each viral capsid shape.
   a. Spherical: Influenza, HIV (MB, p. 484)
   b. Helical: TMV, rabies, measles (MB, p. 484)
   c. Icosahedral: Herpes, chickenpox, polio (MB, p. 484)

6. Which macromolecule is the capsid primarily made up of?
   Protein (MB, p. 484)

7. What is a viral envelope, and where does a virus get one?
   A viral envelope is phospholipid bilayer a virus acquires from the host cell membrane. (MB, p. 484)

8. In what different ways might viruses be classified?
   By capsid, by genome, and/or by the presence or absence of an envelope (MB, p. 484)

9. How is replication in RNA viruses different from DNA viruses?
   When a DNA virus enters a cell, it inserts its genome into the host cell genome and uses the cell
   to begin viral replication. An RNA virus may enter a cell and begin viral replication from its viral
   RNA, or it may make DNA from its RNA and insert the new viral DNA into the host cell genome.
   (MB, pp. 485-486)

10. What is a cell called once it has been infected by a virus? __A provirus (MB, p. 485)__

11. What are the viruses that infect bacteria? __Bacteriophage (MB, p. 486)__

12. What is a bacteria called once it has been infected with a virus? __Prophage (MB, pp. 486-487)__

13. Describe the lytic and lysogenic cycles of viruses in prokaryotes.

The lytic cycle is considered the virulent cycle. The viral genome enters a cell, and viral replication occurs until the host cell ruptures, releasing the newly made viruses. The lysogenic cycle is considered temperate, and the viral genome is inserted into the host cell genome. Host cell division occurs, producing new cells with viral genome. Any or all of these cells may enter the lytic cycle anytime conditions are favorable. Viruses may remain dormant for months or years before they enter the lytic cycle. (MB, pp. 486-487)

14. How do scientists think the first viruses originated?

Viruses likely originated from a naked piece of nucleic acid that entered a cell with a damaged cell membrane. Evolution would have provided the capsid over time. (MB, p. 488)

15. What are vectors, and what are some common vectors?

Vectors are intermediaries that aid in viral transmission such as animals, insects, body fluids, etc. (MB, p. 489)

16. What virus causes chickenpox?

Varicella-zoster, which is a type of herpes virus (MB, p. 489)

17. What is shingles, and who gets shingles?

Shingles is a reactivation of the varicella virus, which has lain dormant in nerve cells. It usually affects adults who previously had chickenpox. It erupts as a painful rash along the path of the infected nerve. (MB, p. 489)

18. What is hepatitis?

Inflammation of the liver caused by hepatitis virus (MB, p. 489)

19. How are the different strains of hepatitis transmitted?

Hepatitis A and hepatitis E are transmitted through fecal contamination of food or water.

Hepatitis B, C, and D are transmitted sexually, through contact with infected blood, and by using contaminated needles (MB, p. 489)

20. What are the symptoms of hepatitis?

Stomach pain and nausea, fever, diarrhea, and jaundice of the skin and sclera (MB, p. 489)

21. What does HIV stand for? Human immunodeficiency virus (MB, p. 490)

22. Explain the mechanics of HIV infection.

The virus enters the host through infected body fluids. HIV is a retrovirus, so using the enzyme reverse transcriptase, it assembles viral DNA from its own RNA genome. The virus first enters the macrophage (type of white blood cell) and begins viral replication, adding host cell markers to the newly made viruses. The newly made viruses with host cell markers are released, infect the host lymphocytes (type of white blood cell), and may lead to AIDS. (MB, pp. 490-491)

23. How is HIV treated? A cocktail of antiviral medications (MB, p. 491)

24. What is AIDS?

AIDS stands for acquired immune deficiency syndrome. People are diagnosed with AIDS if they have HIV infection and at least two other secondary infections, one of which is usually pneumonia. Once diagnosed with AIDS, the only prognosis is death. Not all people infected with HIV develop AIDS. (MB, pp. 490-491) (IV Chapter 24.2, Minute 27)

25. How do some viruses lead to cancer?

If viral DNA is inserted in the host cell genome near oncogenes (genes that control normal cell division), it may cause uncontrolled cell division and result in a tumor. Proto-oncogenes control cell growth, and viral DNA inserted near or in an oncogene or proto-oncogene can lead to uncontrolled cell growth. Some examples: HPV may cause cervical cancer; hepatitis B may lead to liver cancer. (MB, p. 491)

26. What are the three primary actions taken to treat or prevent viral infection?

Vector control, antiviral treatment, and vaccination (MB, p. 492)

27. What is a viroid?

A naked piece of nucleic acid capable of entering a cell and causing disease (MB, p. 494)

28. What is a prion?

A naked piece of protein capable of entering a cell and causing disease (MB, p. 494)

29. Where do new viruses come from?

People visiting islands and countries not previously inhabited (MB, p. 491)

CHAPTER 25: Protists

VOCABULARY

Section 1
1. protist: _____
2. binary fission: _____
3. multiple fission: _____
4. conjugation: _____

Section 2
5. pseudopodium: _____
6. amoeboid movement: _____
7. test: _____
8. cilium: _____
9. pellicle: _____
10. oral groove: _____
11. mouth pore: _____
12. gullet: _____
13. anal pore: _____
14. contractile vacuole: _____
15. macronucleus: _____

7. Some protists exhibit the same alternation of generations that plants do. The parent may reproduce sexually, while its offspring may reproduce asexually. Some protists can reproduce either asexually or sexually depending on environmental favorability. (MB, p. 504)

8. There is so much diversity within the kingdom Protista that some of the organisms in the kingdom have very little similarity. Classifying them into more than one kingdom may allow for a more efficient organization. (MB, p. 502)

9. Binary fission is asexual prokaryotic cell division resulting in two new genetically identical organisms. During conjugation, the DNA of two different organisms is combined to create new and genetically different organisms. (MB, p. 504)

Section 2

1. Protozoa: Free-living heterotrophic amoebas (MB, p. 506)

   Ciliophora: Free-living ciliates with two nuclei (MB, pp. 507–508)

   Sarcomastigophora: Characterized by one or more flagella, heterotrophic, and frequently parasitic (MB, pp. 508–509)

   Apicomplexa: Adult forms have no means of locomotion, and all species are parasitic. (MB, p. 509)

2. Cytoplasm is pushed forward, forming pseudopods, and then the rear cytoplasm is pulled forward. Protozoans use pseudopods to surround and engulf food. (MB, p. 506)

3. They reproduce asexually through binary fission and sexually through conjugation and then fission. (MB, p. 508)

4. Pseudopods, cilia, and flagella respectively (MB, pp. 506–509)

5. Apicomplexans are parasites. They infect a host and use the host for resources, frequently causing illness in the host. (MB, p. 509)

6. Any reasonable answer. Entamoeba histolytica can cause ulcers and amebiasis, Trypanosoma causes sleeping sickness, Plasmodium can cause death, Toxoplasma gondii causes toxoplasmosis, and Cryptosporidium causes flulike symptoms. (MB, pp. 507, 509)

7. Mosquitoes are the vectors of malaria. Controlling the number of mosquitoes would reduce cases of malaria. (MB, p. 509)

8. Since they have no means of locomotion, they must live in hosts as parasites to have a food source. (MB, p. 509)

SECTION REVIEW KEY

Section 1

1. Eukaryotes that cannot be otherwise classified as animals, plants, or fungus (MB, p. 501)

2. It is thought that eukaryotes evolved when a larger prokaryote engulfed a smaller prokaryote and they lived symbiotically together until the smaller prokaryote became mitochondria or chloroplasts. (MB, p. 501)

3. Protists are classified by characteristics that make them mostly animal-like, plantlike, or funguslike organisms. (MB, p. 502)

4. Unicellular protists are single-celled independent living organisms. Some unicellular protists live in colonies but do not exhibit any cell specialization. Multicellular protists do not have true tissues or organs but do exhibit some cell specialization and divisions of labor within the organism. (MB, p. 503)

5. Protists may be autotrophic and photosynthetic or heterotrophic. (MB, p. 503)

6. Pseudopods and cytoplasmic streaming, flagella, or cilia (MB, p. 503)

9. Most likely is a protozoan. It has no cilia or flagella, so it must be an amoeba or an apicomplexan. Apicomplexans form spores, so it must be a protozoan. (MB, pp. 506, 509)

Section 3

1. Unicellular, colonial, filamentous, and multicellular (MB, p. 510)

2. Chlorophyta, Phaeophyta, Rhodophyta, Bacillariophyta, Dinoflagellata, Chrysophyta, and Euglenophyta (MB, pp. 511-513)

3. They have the same type of chlorophylls, they store food as starch, and both have cell walls made of cellulose. (MB, p. 511)

4. Brown algae have a pigment called fucoxanthin that makes them brown. (MB, pp. 511-512)

5. Slime molds are composed of many amoebas and become sessile during their reproductive phase. Water molds are made up of branching filaments. (MB, pp. 514-515)

6. Cellular slime molds are made up of multitudes of amoebas all gathered together, while plasmodial slime molds undergo cell division without cytoplasmic division, so they are a multinucleate glob of cytoplasm with no cell membranes. (MB, p. 514)

7. Because it is composed of individual cells, whereas a true plasmodium is a multinucleate blob of cytoplasm with no cell membranes (MB, p. 514)

8. Any answer that represents the relationship among chytrids, protists, and fungi

9. Bacillariophyta, Chrysophyta, or Dinoflagellata (MB, pp. 512-513)

16. micronucleus: _____

17. flagellum: _____

Section 3

18. alga: _____

19. gametangium: _____

20. phytoplankton: _____

21. thallus: _____

22. accessory pigment: _____

23. diatom: _____

24. shell: _____

25. bioluminescence: _____

26. red tide: _____

27. euglenoid: _____

28. fruiting body: _____

29. water mold: _____

30. plasmodial slime mold: _____

31. cellular slime mold: _____

Biology Coloring Workbook

Complete Chapter 6: Protozoa, Slime Molds, Simple Algae.

PROTISTS CHART

Kingdom Protista is the most diverse of the four eukaryotic kingdoms. Refer back to this chart if the phyla become confusing. It will help you keep them organized.

The kingdom is divided up into three main groups with several phyla or subphyla in each.

The three main groups of protists are plantlike protists, funguslike protists, and animal-like protists. Each phylum is classified into whichever group it most resembles. Some of the organisms fit into two different groups and may be classified differently based on the source.

Plantlike Protists: Algae and Plankton

1. Phylum Chlorophyta (Green algae)
2. Phylum Phaeophyta (Brown algae)
3. Phylum Rhodophyta (Red algae)
4. Phylum Bacillariophyta (Diatoms)
5. Phylum Dinoflagellata (Algae with flagella)
6. Phylum Chrysophyta (Golden algae)
7. Phylum Euglenophyta (Photosynthetic animal-like protists)

Funguslike Protists: Slime and Water Molds

1. Phylum Myxomycota (Plasmodial slime molds)
2. Phylum Dictyostelida (Cellular slime molds)
3. Phylum Oomycota (Water molds)
4. Phylum Chytridiomycota (Water molds)

Animal-Like Protists: Protozoans*

1. Phylum Protozoa (Amoebas)
   a. Subphylum Sarcodina
   b. Subphylum Mycetozoa (Radiolarians)
2. Phylum Ciliaphora (Ciliates)
3. Phylum Sarcomastigophora (Flagellates)
4. Phylum Apicomplexa (Sporozoans)

*Most of these are disease causing or pathogenic.

COMPREHENSION QUESTIONS

1. In which domain are protists classified? _____ Eukarya (MB, p. 501)

2. Through what process are protists thought to have evolved from prokaryotes? Endosymbiosis (MB, p. 501)

3. How are protists classified within the kingdom?
   By their dominant characteristics being more plantlike, funguslike, or animal-like (MB, p. 502)

4. Why is kingdom Protista the most diverse of all kingdoms?
   It includes all of the organisms that are not clearly plant, animal, or fungus and is basically a
   catchall kingdom for organisms that do not fit into any other kingdom. (MB, pp. 501-502)

Animal-Like Protists: Protozoans

5. What two characteristics do all animal-like protists have in common?
   They are all unicellular and heterotrophic. (MB, p. 503)

6. What is the morphology of the protists in the phylum Protozoa? They are amoebas. (MB, p. 506)

7. How do these organisms locomote? Cytoplasmic streaming (MB, p. 506)

8. How do they obtain nutrition? Phagocytosis (MB, p. 506)

9. What is cytoplasmic streaming?
   The pushing of cytoplasm forward, forming pseudopods (false feet) and then pulling in the
   remaining cytoplasm (MB, p. 506)

10. What is phagocytosis?
    A type of endocytosis in which the amoeba surrounds the food with pseudopods and engulfs
    the organism with its plasma membrane (MB, p. 506)

11. What digestive disorder is associated with Entamoeba histolytica? Intestinal ulcers (MB, p. 507)

12. What do the sarcodines and mycetozoans have in common?
    They are both amoebas. (MB, p. 507)

13. How are they different?
    Sarcodines are simple amoebas, while mycetozoans are amoebas living inside a shell with
    holes for their pseudopods to extend through. (MB, p. 507)

14. Which phylum does the Paramecium belong to? Ciliaphora (MB, p. 502)

15. What is a pellicle?
    A flexible membrane under the plasma membrane that gives the organism flexibility and
    allows it to change shape (MB, p. 508)

16. Describe the digestive structures and digestive process of a paramecium.

Cilia surrounding the oral groove sweep food into the oral groove and mouth pore. The food is transferred to the gullet, where it is packed into food vacuoles; there, it is broken down and distributed throughout the organism. Waste is expelled through the anal pore. (MB, p. 508)

17. What is the purpose of a contractile vacuole?

To assist the organism in ridding itself of extra osmotic water (MB, p. 508)

18. What twofold purpose do cilia have? Assist in movement and feeding (MB, pp. 507-508)

19. How do paramecium reproduce? Binary fission or conjugation (MB, p. 508)

20. How many offspring are produced by each reproductive process?

Asexual reproduction results in two identical offspring, while sexual reproduction results in four similar offspring. (MB, p. 508)

21. What is the purpose of both the micronucleus and macronucleus?

The macronucleus controls metabolism and development, and the micronucleus controls cell replication. (MB, p. 508)

22. What do all organisms in the phylum Sarcomastigophora have in common? Flagella (MB, p. 508)

23. What do sarcomastigophorans eat?

Free-living flagellates feed on smaller organisms, while parasitic flagellates feed on host tissues. (MB, pp. 508-509)

24. What parasitic sarcomastigophoran causes sleeping sickness? Trypanosoma (MB, p. 509)

25. What is the vector for this disease?

The tsetse fly or other blood-sucking insects (MB, p. 509)

26. What organisms can become infected with this protist?

Fish, reptiles, amphibians, birds, and mammals (MB, p. 509)

27. Which phylum of animal-like protists kill more people than any other pathogen on Earth?

Apicomplexa (MB, p. 509)

28. What do these protists all have in common?

They have no means of locomotion. (MB, p. 509)

29. How do these organisms move around?

They must be moved by air, fluids, or vectors. (MB, p. 509)

30. Apicomplexans have a specialized set of organelles that help them gain entry to host cells. What is this group of organelles called?

Apical complex (MB, p. 509)

31. Apicomplexans produce infectious reproductive cells with resistant coats called _sporozoites (MB, p. 509)_ .

32. The protist that causes malaria is _Plasmodium (MB, p. 509)_ .

33. The vector for this disease is the _Anopheles mosquito (MB, p. 509)_ .

34. Toxoplasmosis is caused by the protist _Toxoplasma gondii (MB, p. 509)_ .

35. Who is most affected by toxoplasmosis infection? _Unborn fetuses (MB, p. 509)_

36. How is toxoplasmosis spread? _It is usually spread through cat feces. (MB, p. 509)_

37. Cryptosporidium causes flulike symptoms and is spread through _contaminated water or feces of infected animals. (MB, p. 509)_

Plantlike Protists

38. Why are algae not classified as plants?
    They have no true roots, stems, or leaves. (MB, p. 510)

39. What do all algae have in common? _They are all photosynthetic. (MB, p. 510)_

40. How do the algae obtain food? _They are autotrophic; they make their own. (MB, p. 510)_

41. What are pyrenoids?
    Specialized vacuoles for the production and storage of starch (MB, p. 510)

42. What are the end products of photosynthesis? _Carbohydrates and oxygen (MB, p. 510)_

43. What are the four main body forms of algae? Give an organismal example of each.
    a. _Unicellular: Diatoms (MB, p. 510)_
    b. _Colonial: Volvox (MB, p. 510)_
    c. _Filamentous: Spirogyra (MB, p. 510)_
    d. _Multicellular: Kelp (MB, p. 510)_

44. What is the body portion of multicellular algae called? _Thallus (MB, p. 510)_

45. What is the phylum of green algae called? _Chlorophyta (MB, p. 511)_

46. What is the phylum of brown algae called? _Phaeophyta (MB, p. 512)_

47. What is the brown accessory pigment found in brown algae? _Fucoxanthin (MB, p. 512)_

48. Where are brown algae found?
    Cold, rocky coastal waters (MB, p. 512)

49. What is the phylum of red algae called? _Rhodophyta (MB, p. 512)_

50. What is the red accessory pigment found in red algae? _Phycobilin (MB, p. 512)_

51. Where are red algae found? _Deeper ocean waters (MB, p. 512)_

52. What is the phylum of golden algae called? _Chrysophyta (MB, p. 513)_

53. What is the golden accessory pigment found in these algae? _Carotenoids (MB, p. 513)_

54. Where are golden algae found?
    Freshwater lakes and rivers (MB, p. 513)

55. What is the purpose of the cysts these algae form?

Help make them temperature resistant (MB, p. 513)

56. What part do golden algae play in helping to produce underground petroleum deposits?

They store surplus energy as oil so when they break down and decompose. they add to deposits.

(MB, p. 513)

57. Diatoms are part of which phylum of protists? _____ Bacillariophyta (MB, p. 512)

58. Describe the morphology of diatoms.

They have an outer shell made up of two pieces (valves) that fit together like a box and a lid.

(MB, p. 512)

59. The protists that produce bioluminescence and red tide are part of which phylum? Dinoflagellata (MB, p. 513)

60. Why are these flagellated protists not included in the group of animal-like protists?

They are autotrophic rather than heterotrophic. (MB, p. 513)

61. Describe the plantlike and animal-like characteristics of Euglena.

a. _____ Plantlike: Photosynthetic, contractile vacuoles (MB, p. 513)

b. _____ Animal-like: Motile, eyespots, no cell wall (MB, p. 513)

62. What is the common habitat of Euglena?

Fresh water that is polluted, soil, intestines (MB, p. 513)

63. Which protist makes up most of phytoplankton? _____ Bacillariophyta (MB, p. 512)

Funguslike Protists: Slime and Water Molds

64. Where are slime molds found?

On dead or decaying organic matter in damp areas (MB, p. 514)

65. How does their morphology change from their juvenile stage to their adult stage?

During the juvenile stage, the plasmodium is motile and growing. During the adult stage, the

plasmodium becomes sessile and forms fruiting bodies for reproduction. (MB, p. 514)

66. What is a plasmodium? _____ A multinucleate glob of cytoplasm (MB, p. 514)

67. What is the phylum of plasmodial slime molds? _____ Myxomycota (MB, p. 514)

68. How do these organisms locomote?

They creep across the forest floor by cytoplasmic streaming. (MB, p. 514)

69. What do these organisms eat?

They secrete digestive enzymes and absorb the nutrients. (MB, p. 514)

70. When do they enter their reproductive stage?

When food and water become scarce (MB, p. 514)

71. What are fruiting bodies?

Reproductive structures that contain haploid spores (MB, p. 514)

72. What is a pseudoplasm? A collection of individual slime mold cells (MB, p. 514)

73. What is the phylum of cellular slime molds? Dictyostelida (MB, p. 514)

74. When and how do these organisms form a pseudoplasm?

When food and water become scarce, the individual cells emit a chemical that attracts the

individual amoebas together to form the pseudoplasm. (MB, p. 514)

75. What are the two phyla of water molds? Oomycota and Chytridiomycota (MB, p. 515)

76. How are they alike? They are both aquatic and parasitic. (MB, p. 515)

77. How are they different?

Chytridiomycota have flagella, and Oomycota grow and connect to others of the same species

via fertilization tubes. (MB, p. 515)

CHAPTER 29: Plant Structure and Function

VOCABULARY

Section 1

1. parenchyma: _____

2. collenchyma: _____

3. sclerenchyma: _____

4. epidermis: _____

5. cuticle: _____

6. tracheid: _____

7. pit: _____

8. vessel element: _____

9. vessel: _____

10. sieve tube member: _____

11. sieve tube: _____

12. sieve plate: _____

13. companion cell: _____

14. meristem: _____

15. apical meristem: _____

16. lateral meristem: _____

SECTION REVIEW KEY

Section 1

1. Parenchyma are loosely packed, cube-shaped cells with a large central vacuole and thin cell walls. Collenchyma cells have thick irregular cell walls and are usually arranged in strands. Sclerenchyma cells have thick, regular, rigid cell walls. (MB, pp. 583-584)

2. Dermal tissue is made up primarily of parenchyma cells and usually forms the outer layer of the plant or epidermis. Ground tissue is made up of parenchyma, collenchyma, and sclerenchyma cells. It lies just inside the dermal tissue. Vascular tissue is made up primarily of elongated sclerenchyma cells that connect at the ends for conduction. (MB, pp. 584-585)

3. Apical meristems (MB, p. 586)

4. Primary growth is in plant length, and secondary growth is in diameter. (MB, p. 586)

Section 2

1. A taproot is a large single root that grows down. Fibrous roots are numerous hairlike roots that branch. Adventitious roots grow from odd or unusual places like stems or leaves. (MB, pp. 587-589)

2. Root hairs increase surface area for water absorption. (MB, p. 588)

3. The root cap reduces friction and allows the root to move deeper into the soil. (MB, p. 588)

4. Primary growth is in length and secondary growth is in diameter. (MB, pp. 589-590)

5. Roots store water and carbohydrates, provide surface for absorption of nutrients and water, and help anchor the plant into the soil. (MB, pp. 590-591)

6. Fibrous roots are most often seen in small plants that do not grow deep in the soil, such as grass. Taproots grow from plants that need a heavy anchor and to pull water up from deep in the soil. (MB, pp. 587-588)

Section 3

1. Thorny stems protect a plant from herbivores. (MB, p. 592)

2. New growth of tissues occurs at the apical meristem of both roots and stems. (MB, pp. 593-594)

3. Primary growth in monocots is usually quite fast and occurs for the lifetime of the plant, whereas primary growth in dicots is a little slower and becomes secondary to growth in diameter as the plant matures and ages. (MB, p. 594)

4. Springwood forms during periods of heavier rain, while summerwood forms during hot, dry summers. The abrupt change in the type of wood produces the annual rings seen in woody stems. (MB, p. 595)

5. Groundwater enters the roots by osmosis and is pulled up the stem by cohesion and adhesion as the water continues to evaporate from the leaves, creating constant movement of water up as long as it is available. (MB, p. 597)

6. Tree bark contains vascular tissue that is nutritious for squirrels. (MB, p. 594)

7. Living cells contain organelles and cytoplasm that take up space. Dead cells would transport water volume more efficiently. (MB, p. 597)

8. The cells must be connected and be large enough to move sugars around the plant. (MB, p. 596)

Section 4

1. Most leaves are broad for gas exchange and sunlight reception. Carnivorous plants have leaves shaped as traps, which secrete enzymes to digest their contents. Cacti have sharp, pointed leaves to minimize water loss and protect them from herbivores. Some leaves grow as tendrils to give plants support as they wrap the plant around stationary objects. (MB, p. 599)

2. A simple leaf has a single blade, a compound leaf has two or more leaflets, and a doubly compound leaf has leaflets divided a second time into secondary leaflets. (MB, p. 600)

3. The primary function of dermal tissue in leaves is to provide a surface for gas exchange while minimizing water loss from transpiration. The ground tissue functions primarily in photosynthesis, while the vascular tissue conducts water and nutrients throughout the leaf. (MB, pp. 600-601)

4. Guard cells take on water, swelling and bowing in causing the stomata to open. When the guard cells lose water, they shrink and close the stomata. (MB, p. 602)

5. The bottom surface of a leaf has less exposure to the sun, which helps conserve water in the leaf. (MB, pp. 600, 602)

6. Ultraviolet rays are less intense in the winter, and carbon dioxide levels are lower because the greenhouse stays closed to conserve heat, resulting in gasses becoming unbalanced. (MB, p. 602)

7. The plant would die since the stomata would be unable to open in the absence of potassium. (MB, p. 602)

17. vascular cambium: _____

18. cork cambium: _____

Section 2

19. taproot: _____

20. fibrous root system: _____

21. adventitious root: _____

22. root cap: _____

23. root hair: _____

24. cortex: _____

25. endodermis: _____

26. pericycle: _____

27. macronutrient: _____

28. micronutrient: _____

Section 3

29. node: _____

30. internode: _____

31. bud: _____

32. bud scale: _____

33. pith: _____

Biology Coloring Workbook

Complete Chapter 7: The Root, Structure of a Flowering Plant, The Stem, Xylem and Phloem, Transport in Plants, The Leaf.

34. wood:_____

_____

35. heartwood: _____

_____

36. sapwood:_____

_____

37. bark:_____

_____

38. springwood:_____

_____

39. summerwood: _____

_____

40. annual ring: _____

_____

41. source: _____

_____

42. sink:_____

_____

43. translocation: _____

_____

44. pressure-flow hypothesis:_____

_____

45. transpiration: _____

_____

46. cohesion-tension theory: _____

_____

Section 4

47. tendril:_____

_____

48. blade:_____

_____

49. petiole: _____

_____

50. simple leaf:_____

_____

51. compound leaf: _____

_____

52. leaflet: _____

_____

53. mesophyll: _____

_____

54. palisade mesophyll: _____

_____

55. spongy mesophyll: _____

_____

56. vein: _____

_____

57. venation: _____

_____

58. parallel venation: _____

_____

59. net venation: _____

_____

60. guard cell: _____

_____

COMPREHENSION QUESTIONS

1. As a review, briefly describe three structures found in plant cells that are not found in animal cells.
   a. Chloroplasts: Organelles that contain chlorophyll for photosynthesis (MB, p. 89)
   b. Cell wall: Outer layer of polysaccharide for strength and protection (MB, p. 88)
   c. Contractile vacuole: Water collection reservoir for water storage and management (MB, p. 83)

2. What are the three basic plant cell types?
   Parenchyma, collenchyma, and sclerenchyma (MB, p. 583)

3. What is the primary function of parenchyma cells?
   Metabolic functions such as photosynthesis (MB, p. 583)

4. What are four physical characteristics of parenchyma cells?
   a. Cube-shaped or elongated (MB, p. 583)
   b. Loosely packed (MB, p. 583)
   c. Large central vacuole (MB, p. 583)
   d. Thin, flexible cell walls (MB, p. 583)

5. Where are parenchyma cells found most abundantly?
   Flexible green stems and fleshy parts of fruit (MB, p. 583)

6. What is the primary function of collenchyma cells?
   Support of elongating plants (MB, p. 582)

7. What are the dominant physical characteristics of collenchyma cells?
    Thick, irregularly shaped cell walls that grow in groups of strands (e.g., strands making up a
    celery stalk) (MB, pp. 583-584)

8. What is the primary function of sclerenchyma cells?
    Strength and support (MB, p. 584)

9. What are the dominant physical characteristics of sclerenchyma cells?
    Thick, rigid cell walls that are irregularly shaped. They die and remain when they are mature
    (e.g., nut shells). (MB, p. 584)

10. Groups of different cells working together form tissues (MB, p. 584).

11. What are the three different types of plant tissue?
    Dermal tissue, ground tissue, and vascular tissue (MB, p. 584)

12. What makes these tissues different from one another?
    Different quantities of the three cell types arranged in different patterns (MB, p. 584)

13. When different plant tissues are grouped together, they make up the plant organs. What are the three
    major plant organs? Roots, stems, and leaves (MB, p. 584)

14. Which cell type is found most abundantly in dermal tissue? Parenchyma (MB, p. 584)

15. Where is dermal tissue found in most plants? Epidermis (MB, p. 584)

16. What are the primary functions of dermal tissue?
    Absorption in roots; gas exchange and protection in stems and leaves (MB, p. 584)

17. Where is the ground tissue found in most plants?
    Just under the dermal tissue (MB, pp. 584-585)

18. Which cell types make up ground tissue?
    It is composed of all three cell types, with parenchyma cells being the most common.
    (MB, pp. 584-585)

19. What are the primary functions of ground tissue?
    In roots and stems, ground tissue functions in support and storage. In leaves, ground tissue
    functions primarily in photosynthesis. (MB, pp. 584-585)

20. Which cell types make up vascular tissue?
    Sclerenchyma and parenchyma cells (MB, pp. 584-585)

21. What are the primary functions of vascular tissue?
    Transport of water and nutrients and support (MB, pp. 584-585)

22. Where is the vascular tissue found?
    It is the innermost tissue of the root, stem, or leaf. (MB, pp. 584-585)

23. What are the two different types of vascular tissue? Xylem and phloem (MB, p. 585)

24. What is the primary function of xylem?

To move water and nutrients in one direction up from the roots to the stems and leaves
(MB, p. 585)

25. What are the two different types of sclerenchyma cells forming the xylem?

Tracheids and vessel elements (MB, p. 585)

26. What are the primary structural differences between these two types of cells?

Tracheids have tapered ends with pits scattered throughout for water to move laterally from
one tracheid to another. Vessel elements have open ends and stack to form longer vessels for
water to move up from the roots to the stems and leaves. (MB, p. 585)

27. What is the primary function of phloem?

To move water and molecules in any direction for use or storage within the plant (MB, p. 585)

28. What type of cells make up the phloem?

Parenchyma cells called sieve tube members (MB, p. 585)

29. Describe the structure of a sieve tube member.

The sieve tube members stack to form long sieve tubes for conduction. Sieve plates in the
ends of the sieve tube members allow water to pass from one sieve tube member to the next.
Parenchyma cells called companion cells lie adjacent to the sieve tubes to aid the sieve tubes
in transport and storage of sugars made by the plant through photosynthesis. (MB, p. 585)

Plant Growth

30. What is the area of a plant where cell division and growth occur? Meristem (MB, p. 586)

31. What are the different types of meristems?

Apical, intercalary, and lateral

(Primary and secondary are also acceptable answers. Primary meristems include apical and
intercalary and are responsible for growth in length. Secondary meristems include lateral, both
vascular and cork cambium, and are responsible for growth in diameter.) (MB, p. 586)

32. Where are apical meristems located?

At the ends of roots and the tips of stems where plants grow in length (MB, p. 586)

33. Where are intercalary meristems located?

Between the base and tips of leaves and stems in certain plants like grass for rapid growth in length (MB, p. 586)

34. What are the two different types of lateral meristems?

Vascular cambium and cork cambium (MB, p. 586)

35. What type of growth is associated with the lateral meristems?

Growth in width or diameter of the plant (MB, p. 586)

36. Where are lateral meristems located?

They are located near the outsides of stems and roots. Vascular cambium lies between the xylem and phloem, while cork cambium lies outside the phloem. (MB, p. 586)

37. What is the difference between the two types of lateral or secondary meristems?

Vascular cambium produces more vascular tissue, while cork cambium produces cork cells that replace the epidermis in woody stems and roots such as those found in trees. (MB, p. 586)

38. What is the difference between primary and secondary growth?

Primary growth is in length and occurs at the apical or intercalary meristems, while secondary growth is in diameter and occurs at the lateral meristems. (MB, p. 586)

Roots

39. What are the three different types of roots? Give one example of each.

a. Taproots: Radish, carrot, most woody trees (MB, p. 587)

b. Fibrous roots: Grass, lilies (MB, p. 587)

c. Adventitious roots: Roots that grow from stems or leaves, seen in ivy, squash, or corn (MB, p. 588)

40. Where is the root cap found? What is its purpose?

The root cap is found on the tip of the apical meristem and produces slime to allow the root to grow easily through packed dirt. (MB, p. 588)

41. What purpose do root hairs serve?

They increase surface area of the root for intake of water and nutrients, they aid in anchoring the plant in the soil, and they may store starch for energy when needed. (MB, p. 588)

Vascular plants are divided into two groups, monocots and dicots. Monocots are plants with parallel veins and fibrous roots such as grass, corn, or lilies. Dicots are plants with netted veins and taproots such as oak trees or roses.

With regard to roots, refer to Figure 29-6 in the text to fill in the blanks of questions 43-48.

42. The outermost tissue of the root is called the epidermis (Dermal tissue is acceptable) (MB, p. 589)

43. Just inside the epidermis, ground tissue forms the cortex (MB, p. 589) and endodermis (MB, p. 589) .

44. The vascular (MB, p. 589) tissue is found just inside the endodermis.

45. Describe the organization of the vascular tissue in a dicot root.

     Xylem makes up the center core and forms an X-shaped structure with phloem embedded around the xylem. (MB, p. 589)

46. Describe the organization of the vascular tissue in a monocot root.

     A pith of parenchyma cells forms in the center with patches of xylem that circle the pith. The phloem is arranged in patches between the xylem. (MB, p. 589)

47. What is the pericycle, and where is it found?

     The pericycle is the outermost layer of vascular tissue that lies just under the endodermis. Cell division here gives rise to lateral roots. (MB, p. 590)

48. List three functions of plant roots.

     Anchor the plant in the soil; absorb water and nutrients from the soil; store water and sugars (MB, p. 590)

49. How many different minerals are absorbed by plant roots? 13 (MB, pp. 590-591)

Stems

50. What are the two primary stem types? Give one example of each.

    a. Woody: Tree trunks, rose stems (MB, p. 592)

    b. Non-woody: Flower and vegetable stems (MB, p. 592)

51. Stems grow in a large variety of different forms as adaptations to the environment. List four different types of stems and give one example of each.

    a. Stolons: Grow along the surface of the soil and produce new plants (e.g., strawberry) (MB, p. 592)

    b. Tubers: Store starch as energy (e.g., potato) (MB, p. 592)

    c. Fleshy stems: Store water (e.g., cactus) (MB, p. 592)

    d. Thorny stems: Protect the plant from animals (e.g., rosebush) (MB, p. 592)

52. With regard to stems, refer to Figure 29-9 in the text to label the diagram and briefly describe the function of each stem structure labeled.

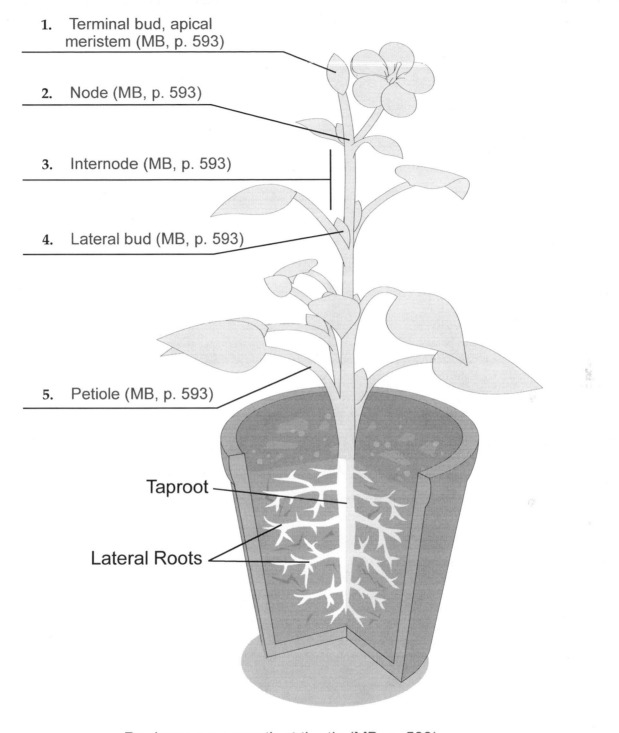

1. Terminal bud, apical meristem (MB, p. 593)
2. Node (MB, p. 593)
3. Internode (MB, p. 593)
4. Lateral bud (MB, p. 593)
5. Petiole (MB, p. 593)

Taproot

Lateral Roots

a. Apical meristem: _Produces new growth at the tip (MB, p. 593)_
b. Terminal bud: _Covers the tip of each stem (MB, p. 593)_
c. Node: _Location of leaf attachment (MB, p. 593)_
d. Internode: _Region of stem between nodes (MB, p. 593)_
e. Lateral bud: _Located at each leaf attachment (MB, p. 593)_
f. Petiole: _Small stem that attaches the leaf to the main stem (MB, p. 593)_

53. What are bud scales, and what are their purpose?

Bud scales are specialized leaves for the protection of the apical meristem. In cold climates, the terminal bud opens and bud scales fall off when the dormant season ends and the weather warms. (MB, p. 593)

54. In stems, the apical meristem gives rise to which tissue types?

All three: dermal, ground, and vascular (MB, pp. 593-594)

Refer to Figure 29-10 in the text to answer questions 56-59.

55. What is the outermost covering of the stem, and what is its function?

The epidermis protects and reduces water loss while still allowing for gas exchange. (MB, p. 594)

56. Contrast the arrangement of xylem and phloem in the stem vs. the root.

The xylem and phloem of the stem are arranged in bundles much closer to the outer dermal tissue especially in dicot stems, not at the center as they are in a root. Monocot stems have vascular bundles scattered throughout the ground tissue. (MB, p. 594)

57. What makes up the center of a stem?

Ground tissue forms the pith and is made up primarily of collenchyma cells. (MB, p. 594)

58. Where are the lateral meristems in dicot stems located?

Between the xylem and phloem of a vascular bundle (MB, p. 594)

59. Xylem production in stems is usually greater than phloem production to produce wood. What are the two types of wood found in stems? How are they different?

Heartwood is in the center of the stem and is darker from buildup of organic molecules with age. Heartwood usually stops water transport as it ages. Sapwood is the lighter-colored wood on the outside and transports most of the water and nutrients up the stem. (MB, pp. 594-595)

60. What is tree bark?

Bark is a protective outside covering of woody plants made up of cork, cork cambium, and phloem. (MB, p. 595)

61. What is secondary growth of a stem?

An increase in thickness or diameter of a stem (MB, pp. 594-595)

62. Secondary growth of a stem produces the colored rings seen in stems, particularly large woody tree trunks. What are these two different types of wood and why do they form?

Springwood forms when water is plentiful; the vascular cambium makes new xylem cells that are thin walled and wide. Summerwood forms when water is limited; the vascular cambium makes xylem cells that are thick walled and small. (MB, p. 595)

63. What produces one annual ring in a tree trunk?

One layer of springwood and one layer of summerwood represent one year of secondary tree growth. (MB, p. 595)

64. What are the primary functions of a stem?

Transportation of nutrients and water from roots to leaves, storage of water and sugars, support and structure (MB, pp. 596-597)

65. What is the specialized process of moving water and nutrients up from the roots of a plant, through the stem, and out through the leaves?

Transpiration (MB, p. 597)

66. What two properties cause water to move up roots and stems?

Cohesion and adhesion (MB, p. 597)

67. How do these two properties cause water to move up against gravity?

Cohesion accounts for water's attraction to the walls of the vascular tissue. Adhesion accounts for the water's attraction to itself. As water evaporates from the leaf surface, the water column is more subject to tension. Since water is attracted to water, it can't move apart; it is attracted to the xylem walls, so it can't pull away. It can only move up the trunk of the tree. As it moves up, more water can move into the roots from the soil. (MB, p. 597)

68. Sugars, plant hormones, and organic compounds are moved about the plant, in any direction, through the phloem. Most of the sugars a plant produces are from the leaves. What is the process called where sugars are moved from their production site to their storage site?

Translocation (MB, p. 596)

69. Storage areas within the stems and roots are called the sink (MB, p. 596)

70. What is the pressure-flow hypothesis of translocation?

Newly produced sugars are actively moved into the sieve tubes from the source. Water from vessel elements now flows into sieve tubes by osmosis. A positive pressure builds up at the source end as sugars are actively transported out of the sieve tube into the sink, allowing water to also move out of the sink by osmosis and reducing pressure at the sink. (MB, p. 596)

Leaves

71. The most common leaf shape is the blade. List three other types of leaves and on what type of plant they might be found.

    a. Tendrils: Modified leaves that wrap or wind around objects for extra support of a vine or stem (e.g., peas and pumpkins) (MB, p. 599)

    b. Food traps: Modified leaves found in plants with poor soil. Plants develop ways to obtain nutrients from bugs and small animals (e.g., Venus flytraps and pitcher plants). (MB, p. 599)

    c. Spines: Modified leaves that are sharp or pointy. They help to limit water loss in desert plants or offer protection to plants that are likely to be eaten by animals (e.g. cacti or barberry). (MB, p. 599)

72. Label the diagrams below to indicate the different leaf arrangements.

    a. Simple blade (MB, p. 600)   b. Compound leaf (MB, p. 600)   c. Doubly compound leaf (MB, p. 600)

73. The broad flat portion of the leaf is called the blade. What major metabolic process happens within the blade of the leaf? _____ Photosynthesis (MB, p. 600)

74. What are the veins of a leaf?
    The arrangement of the bundles of vascular tissue that carry water and nutrients throughout the leaves (MB, p. 600)

75. What are the two main venation patterns seen commonly in leaves?
    Net venation, where the vascular bundles branch into smaller veins (seen in dicots), and parallel venation, where the vascular bundles are arranged in straight rows (seen in monocots) (MB, p. 600)

76. What is the petiole?
    The convergence of the veins that attach the leaf to the stem (MB, p. 600)

77. Where is the dermal tissue of a leaf located?
    It forms the epidermis, covering the top and bottom of the leaf. (MB, p. 600)

78. What is the cuticle?
    A waxy coating on the surface of the epidermis to help conserve water and protect the leaf (MB, p. 600)

79. What are stomata?

A specialized set of cells that form a pore to allow CO_2 in and O_2 and water out (MB, p. 600)

80. Where are stomata found?

They are embedded in the epidermis and scattered over the top and/or bottom surfaces of a leaf. (MB, p. 600)

81. Explain how stomata work.

Plants must balance opening the stomata for gas exchange with closing them to prevent transpiration and excessive water loss. Two specialized cells called guard cells form each pore. These guard cells are controlled by the amount of H_2O they hold. K^+ is pumped in by day, causing water to move into guard cells by osmosis. The guard cells swell, causing them to bow apart and form a pore. This process is reversed at night. (MB, p. 602)

82. Under what other circumstances might stomata close? _____ Water shortage (MB, p. 602)

83. When do most plants keep their stomata open, and why?

Most plants open their stomata by day since that is when the sun shines and photosynthesis occurs. The plant's need for CO_2 is the greatest when the carbon is needed to make sugars and oxygen is released as a waste product. (MB, p. 602)

84. What function do the epidermal hairs on the surface of a leaf serve?

Protect the leaf from insects and too much sun (MB, p. 601)

Refer to Figure 29-15 in the text to complete questions 86-90.

85. Where is the ground tissue located in a leaf?

Just under and above the epidermal layers (MB, p. 601)

86. What type of cells make up the bulk of the ground tissue?

Chlorophyll-rich parenchyma cells (MB, p. 601)

87. What are the two different layers of ground tissue called?

Palisade mesophyll and spongy mesophyll (MB, p. 601)

88. How do these layers differ from each other?

The palisade mesophyll is the area where most photosynthesis occurs. It is made up of tightly packed, elongated parenchyma cells. The spongy mesophyll is beneath the palisade mesophyll and is made up of loosely packed parenchyma cells that make space for the vascular bundles to travel through, bringing water and nutrients for photosynthesis. (MB, pp. 600-601)

89. Label the diagram below.

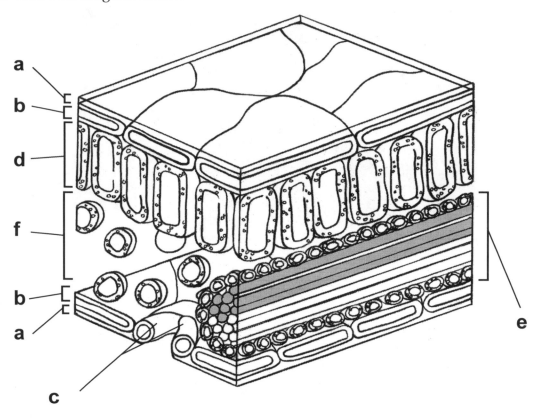

a. Cuticle (MB, p. 601)
b. Epidermal cells (MB, p. 601)
c. Guard cells/stomata (MB, p. 601)
d. Palisade mesophyll (MB, p. 601)
e. Vascular bundle/vein (MB, p. 601)
f. Spongy mesophyll (MB, p. 601)

90. What factors might limit photosynthesis?

Water shortage, water loss, poor soil nutrition (MB, p. 601)

91. How are the leaves of plants that live in full bright sun different from those that grow better in shady spots?

Leaves that develop in full sun are thicker and have less surface area and more

chloroplasts per area. Leaves that develop in shade are thinner and have fewer

chloroplasts that do not overlap. (MB, p. 601)

92. List one or two other ways plants might adapt to intensely sunny habitats.

They may be covered with hair or only partially project above ground. They may develop

specialized leaf structures such as cacti. (MB, p. 601)

THIRD TRIMESTER

SECTION REVIEW KEY

Section 1

1. Animals are all heterotrophic, most are multicellular, reproduce sexually, and exhibit some type of movement. (MB, p. 651)

2. Nervous tissue processes incoming sensory information and sends signals to muscles, which allows the animal to respond to the information. (MB, p. 652)

3. It is thought that early protists lived in colonies, and over time, groups of cells within the colony began to carry out specialized functions until the colony developed into a loosely connected organism. (MB, p. 653)

4. Notochord, pharyngeal pouches, and a post anal tail (MB, p. 654)

5. Bilateral symmetry (MB, p. 655)

6. The presence or absence of true tissues, the number of tissue layers, coelom type, and the presence of a notochord or dorsal nerve cord (MB, pp. 653-654)

Section 2

1. The purpose of an outer body covering on most terrestrial animals is primarily to conserve water and protect the internal organs. (MB, p. 660)

2. An exoskeleton is a tough outer body covering that protects the organism and is shed and replaced as the organism grows. An endoskeleton is a bony or cartilaginous framework inside the organism that grows as the organism grows. (MB, pp. 658, 660)

3. An open circulatory system is commonly seen in less complex animals and consists of a heart and vessels that pump into an open coelom where gas and nutrients are exchanged before the blood or hemolymph returns to vessels that lead to the heart. A closed circulatory system contains the blood in vessels as it travels through the organism and returns to the heart and lungs where gas exchange occurs. (MB, p. 658)

4. All vertebrates and some invertebrates exhibit a high degree of cephalization. Invertebrates usually exhibit simpler response patterns and less organization than vertebrates. (MB, p. 659)

5. Most invertebrates undergo direct development with a larval stage, while all vertebrates undergo direct development and begin life as nymphs. (MB, p. 659)

CHAPTER 32: Introduction to Animals

VOCABULARY

Section 1

1. **animal:** _____

2. **vertebrate:** _____

3. **invertebrate:** _____

4. **specialization:** _____

5. **ingestion:** _____

6. **zygote:** _____

7. **differentiation:** _____

8. **chordate:** _____

9. **notochord:** _____

10. **dorsal nerve cord:** _____

11. **pharyngeal pouch:** _____

12. **symmetry:** _____

13. **radial symmetry:** _____

14. **dorsal:** _____

15. **ventral:** _____

16. **anterior:** _____

Section 3

1. Fertilization, cleavage, blastula formation, and gastrulation (MB, pp. 663-664)

2. Endoderm forms most of the internal organs and the reproductive system. Mesoderm gives rise to the bones and muscles. The ectoderm becomes the skin and nervous system. (MB, p. 664)

3. Protostomes undergo indirect development, spiral cleavage, and schizocoely, and the blastopore becomes the mouth. Deuterostomes undergo direct development, radial cleavage, and enterocoely, and the blastopore becomes the anus. (MB, pp. 665-666)

4. In schizocoely, the mesoderm forms at the junction of the endoderm and ectoderm. In enterocoely, the mesoderm forms at the top of the archenteron. (MB, p. 666)

5. In indeterminate cleavage, if the blastula splits early enough, the cells have the ability to form two complete and identical organisms. (MB, p. 666)

17. posterior:_____

_____

18. bilateral symmetry: _____

_____

19. cephalization: _____

_____

20. germ layer: _____

_____

Section 2

21. segmentation: _____

_____

22. exoskeleton:_____

_____

23. gill:_____

_____

24. open circulatory system: _____

_____

25. closed circulatory system:_____

_____

26. hermaphrodite: _____

_____

27. larva: _____

_____

28. endoskeleton: _____

_____

29. vertebra: _____

_____

30. integument: _____

_____

31. lung:_____

_____

32. kidney: _____

_____

Section 3

33. fertilization: _____

_____

34. cleavage: _____

_____

35. blastula: _____

_____

36. gastrulation: _____

_____

37. gastrula: _____

_____

38. archenteron: _____

_____

39. blastopore: _____

_____

40. ectoderm: _____

_____

41. endoderm: _____

_____

42. mesoderm: _____

_____

43. acoelomate: _____

_____

44. pseudocoelom: _____

_____

45. coelom: _____

_____

46. protostome: _____

_____

47. deuterostome: _____

_____

48. schizocoely: _____

_____

49. enterocoely: _____

_____

COMPREHENSION QUESTIONS

1. What are the four characteristics all animals have in common?

   They are all multicellular, are heterotrophic, exhibit some type of movement, and reproduce sexually. (MB, p. 651)

2. What is cell specialization?

   Cells developing the capability of carrying out different functions (MB, p. 651)

3. What is cell differentiation?

   Cells developing different structural characteristics for the purpose of performing different functions (MB, p. 652)

4. Groups of cells working together to form a function are called ___tissues (MB, p. 651)___.

5. Organisms that must consume other organisms for energy are said to be ___heterotrophic (MB, p. 652)___.

6. Asexual reproduction produces offspring that are ___identical to each other and the parent cell___ (MB, p. 652).

7. Sexual reproduction produces offspring that are ___similar but different from each other and the parent cell (MB, p. 652)___.

8. What is an advantage of each type of reproduction?

   Asexual reproduction does not require gene recombination, so no other organism or DNA is needed. Sexual reproduction produces endless genetic variability and strengthens a species over time. (MB, p. 652)

9. Movement in most animals occurs because of the interrelationship of which two tissue types?

   Muscle tissue and nervous tissue (MB, p. 652)

10. Phylogenetic diagrams show ___the evolutionary relationship of different species (MB, p. 652)___.

11. Animals are classed into phyla based on ___morphology or body plan, embryonic development, and rRNA sequences (MB, p. 653)___.

12. What three basic morphologies are used to classify animals? Give one example of each.

    a. ___No symmetry or asymmetry: Sponges (MB, pp. 653, 655)___

    b. ___Radial symmetry: Jellies (MB, pp. 653, 655)___

    c. ___Bilateral symmetry: Kangaroos (MB, pp. 653, 655)___

13. Describe radial symmetry.

    Radially symmetric animals have distinctly different top and bottom halves but no distinguishable right, left, front, or back halves. (MB, p. 655)

14. Describe bilateral symmetry.

Bilaterally symmetric animals have distinctly different top, bottom, front, and back halves with mirror-imaged right and left halves. (MB, p. 655)

15. What is cephalization?

A concentration of sensory structures such as eyes and brain at the anterior or front end of an animal (MB, p. 655)

16. Which body plan typically exhibits the highest levels of cephalization, and why is it beneficial?

Bilaterally symmetric animals exhibit the most cephalization. Cephalization allows the animal's sensory structures to encounter the world before its body, so incoming information about the animal's environment can be interpreted and the body made to respond accordingly. (MB, p. 655)

17. Label the surfaces of the animals below.

Dorsal or posterior (MB, p. 655)
Superior (MB, p. 655)
Anterior (MB, p. 655)
Dorsal (MB, p. 655)
Posterior (MB, p. 655)
Ventral or anterior (MB, p. 655)
Inferior (MB, p. 655)
Ventral (MB, p. 655)

18. What are germ layers?

Embryonic tissues that develop from the first cells of a new organism (MB, p. 655)

19. What are the three germ layers, and what main structures develop from each layer?

The ectoderm becomes the skin and nervous system. The mesoderm becomes the muscles, bones, and cardiovascular system. The endoderm becomes the visceral organs. (MB, p. 664)

20. Which phylum of invertebrates has no tissues?

Porifera, more commonly known as sponges (MB, p. 653)

21. Which two phyla of invertebrates develop from only two germ layers?

Cnidaria, more commonly known as jellies, and Ctenophora, which include the comb jellies (MB, p. 653)

22. What is a coelom?

A coelom is a fluid-filled body cavity. (MB, p. 665)

23. What is the distinguishing factor between vertebrates and invertebrates?

A bony spinal column and a spinal cord (MB, p. 651)

24. What is segmentation?

The same or similar repeating body structures or units (MB, p. 657)

25. What types of body support are seen in invertebrates? In vertebrates?

Invertebrates may exhibit fluid support, a simple skeleton, or an exoskeleton. Vertebrates have endoskeletons. (MB, p. 658)

26. Describe the different types of respiration seen in invertebrates and in vertebrates.

Invertebrates may respire by simple diffusion of gasses, through gills or lungs, or across their skin or tegument. Vertebrates respire through gills or lungs. (MB, pp. 658, 660)

27. Describe the circulatory systems seen in invertebrates and in vertebrates.

Invertebrates may have no circulatory system, a simple open circulatory system, or a more complex closed circulatory system. All vertebrates have closed circulatory systems. (MB, pp. 658, 660)

28. What is the difference between an open and a closed circulatory system?

An open circulatory system utilizes a pump that sends blood or hemolymph into vessels and then into an open coelom where gasses diffuse into and out of the tissue cells. A closed circulatory system pumps the blood through vessels where gasses diffuse across the vessel walls into the tissue cells. (MB, pp. 658, 660)

29. Describe digestion and excretion in invertebrates and in vertebrates.

Digestion in invertebrates ranges from diffusion and osmosis across cells, to simple one-opening systems where food enters and waste exits from the same opening, to more complex one-way gut tubes with a single opening for food and a different opening for waste. Vertebrates all have one-way gut tubes. (MB, pp. 658, 660)

30. An organism with both male and female reproductive organs is a ___hermaphrodite (MB, p. 659)___.

31. When an invertebrate embryo undergoes indirect development, it begins its life as a <u>larva (MB, p. 659)</u>.
Direct development embryos begin life as <u>nymphs (MB, p. 659)</u>

32. What are the benefits of indirect development?
Indirect development allows the juveniles to exploit different foods and habitats from the
adults, eliminating competition for resources. (MB, p. 659)

33. What is cleavage?
The series of cell divisions that occur immediately following fertilization (MB, p. 664)

34. What is a blastula?
A hollow ball of cells produced by cleavage (MB, p. 664)

35. What is gastrulation?
The collapse of the blastula to produce a multilayered, cup-shaped embryo (MB, p. 664)

36. What is the archenteron?
The archenteron is the cavity formed by gastrulation that will become the gut tube as the
embryo matures. (MB, p. 664)

37. What is the blastopore?
The blastopore is the open end of the archenteron, which will become the organism's mouth
or anus depending on which pattern of development it undergoes. (MB, p. 664)

38. When does an organism change from a zygote to an embryo?
At gastrulation (MB, p. 664)

39. What is an animal with no body cavity called?
An acoelomate (MB, p. 665)

40. What is an animal with a body cavity not completely lined by mesoderm called?
A pseudocoelomate (MB, p. 665)

41. What are animals with at least one body cavity fully lined with mesoderm called?
Coelomates (MB, p. 665)

42. What are the two distinct patterns of development that animals undergo?
Protostome or deuterostome (MB, p. 665)

43. What is the fate of the blastopore in both types of development?
In protostomes, the blastopore will eventually become the mouth. In deuterostomes, it will
become the anus. (MB, p. 665)

44. What is the difference between determinate and indeterminate cleavage?

With determinate cleavage seen in protostomes, the path of each new developing cell is fixed early in its life so that if the blastula were to become separated, it would grow into different halves of the organism and likely die. With indeterminate cleavage seen in deuterostomes, the path of developing cells is fixed much later and the cells have the ability to change fate so that if the blastula were to become split or separated, two identical and complete organisms would ultimately form. (MB, p. 666)

45. What is the difference between schizocoely and enterocoely?

Schizocoely is coelom formation in protostomes where the mesoderm begins to form at the bottom of the gastrula where the ectoderm and endoderm merge. The mesoderm will form pouches that travel upward toward the top of the gastrula, and the pouches will ultimately become the coelom. Enterocoely is coelom formation in deuterostomes where the mesoderm begins to form at the top of the archenteron and travels downward to where the endoderm and ectoderm join. The mesoderm forms pouches that will become the coelom as the organism continues to mature. (MB, p. 666)

46. Fill in the phylum name.

Sponges _____ Porifera _____

Common jellies, coral, anemones _____ Cnidaria _____

Comb jellies _____ Ctenophora _____

Flatworms, flukes, tapeworms _____ Platyhelminthes _____

Roundworms and hookworms _____ Nematoda _____

Snails, clams, oysters, squid, octopi _____ Mollusca _____

Garden worms and leeches _____ Annelida _____

Insects, crustaceans, centipedes, spiders _____ Arthropoda _____

Sea stars_____ Echinodermata _____

Fish, amphibians, reptiles, birds, mammals _____ Chordata _____ (MB, p. 653) _____

47. Based on your comparison of vertebrates and invertebrates, in which of these two groups do you think there is more diversity? Why?

Invertebrates are much more diverse. Their systems range from very simple to very complex. Vertebrate organisms are very similar, and there are few differences between their systems. (MB, p. 654)

SECTION REVIEW KEY

Chapter 33, Section 1

1. They both form the skeleton of sponges. But spongin is a flexible protein, while spicules are hard, rigid calcium carbonate or silicon dioxide. (MB, pp. 673-674)

2. Most sponges filter food from the water that passes through their body, but there are sponges that have coiled filaments that can snare smaller animals and pull them into cells specialized for feeding. (MB, p. 674)

3. Gemmules are food-filled internal buds from sponges that can survive harsh conditions and regenerate again when conditions become favorable. (MB, p. 675)

4. Amoebocytes are sponge cells that carry sperm to the egg cells. (MB, p. 675)

5. Sponges give rise to flagellated larvae that can swim and establish new sponge colonies far away from the parent colony. (MB, p. 675)

6. Spongin is flexible and can withstand manipulation. (MB, p. 673)

Chapter 33, Section 2

1. All cnidarians are made up of two cell layers and have a gastrovascular cavity and a nerve net with cnidocytes for obtaining food and defense. (MB, p. 676)

2. Nematocysts capture or paralyze prey and then tentacles push the food into the mouth. (MB, p. 677)

3. Nerve net (MB, p. 677)

4. Hydrozoa: colonial medusa (MB, p. 678)
   Cubozoa: cube-shaped medusa (MB, p. 680)
   Scyphozoa: common jellyfish (MB, p. 680)
   Anthozoa: coral or sea anemones (MB, p. 681)

5. Cilia, colloblasts, and apical organs (MB, p. 682)

Chapter 34, Section 1

1. They have no body cavity, and the endoderm and mesoderm are pressed against each other. (MB, p. 689)

2. Flame cells are located in the planarian's excretory system, and their purpose is to collect excess water that necessarily osmoses into the organism and excretes it out. (MB, p. 690)

3. Cerebral ganglia and eyespots are both located anteriorly. (MB, p. 691)

VOCABULARY

Chapter 33, Section 1

1. sponge: _____

2. sessile: _____

3. choanocyte: _____

4. ostium: _____

5. osculum: _____

6. spongin: _____

7. spicule: _____

8. filter feeding: _____

9. amoebocyte: _____

10. gemmule: _____

11. regeneration: _____

12. hermaphrodite: _____

Chapter 33, Section 2

13. medusa: _____

14. polyp: _____

15. epidermis: _____

4. Flukes sexually reproduce inside human blood vessels. They can become so numerous that they block blood vessels and infiltrate organs, causing irritation and tissue damage. The disease is called schistosomiasis and can result in death. (MB, pp. 692-693)

5. Tapeworms absorb nutrients through their tegument, and nutrients are assimilated directly into the parasites' tissues. A digestive system is unnecessary. (MB, p. 693)

6. If a parasite kills its host, it will die as well or need to find a new host, which would be difficult for most internal parasites. (MB, p. 691)

7. Asexual reproduction is advantageous during unfavorable environmental conditions when populations are compromised or in decline due to lack of food or habitat. A hermaphroditic organism can self-fertilize ensuring, the continued propagation of the species. (MB, p. 689)

8. Treat the freshwater supplies for the parasite, eliminate the number of snails, or restrict human access to infected waters. (MB, pp. 692-693)

16. gastrodermis: _____
_____

17. mesoglea: _____
_____

18. gastrovascular cavity: _____
_____

19. tentacle: _____
_____

20. cnidocyte: _____
_____

21. nematocyst: _____
_____

22. nerve net: _____
_____

23. planula: _____
_____

24. coral reef: _____
_____

25. colloblast: _____
_____

26. apical organ: _____
_____

27. bioluminescence: _____
_____

Chapter 34, Section 1

28. pharynx: _____
_____

29. flame cell: _____
_____

30. cerebral ganglion: _____
_____

31. eyespot: _____
_____

32. fluke: _____
_____

33. tegument: _____
_____

Chapter 34, Section 2

1. Flatworms are acoelomates and have digestive tracts with only one opening. Roundworms and rotifers both have one-way digestive systems with two openings, and they are both pseudocoelomates. (MB, p. 695)

2. The primary host releases the eggs in feces onto vegetation or into the water. The secondary host is contaminated when infected food and water are consumed. (MB, p. 696)

3. Roundworm bodies are well-adapted to easily move through host tissues. They also have a noncellular cuticle that protects them from the host immune system. (MB, pp. 695-697)

4. The cilia surrounding a rotifer's mouth functions to sweep food particles into the mouth. (MB, p. 698)

Biology Coloring Workbook

Complete Chapter 8: Phylum Porifera, Phylum Cnidaria, Phylum Platyhelminthes, Phylum Nematoda.

34. primary host: _____

_____

35. intermediate host: _____

_____

36. schistosomiasis: _____

_____

37. scolex: _____

_____

38. proglottid: _____

_____

39. cyst: _____

_____

Chapter 34, Section 2

40. roundworm: _____

_____

41. cuticle: _____

_____

42. hookworm: _____

_____

43. trichinosis: _____

_____

44. pinworm: _____

_____

45. filarial worm: _____

_____

46. elephantiasis: _____

_____

47. rotifer: _____

_____

48. mastax: _____

_____

49. cloaca: _____

_____

50. parthenogenesis: _____

_____

COMPREHENSION QUESTIONS

Phylum Porifera

1. Sponges are simple organisms made up of specialized cells but no true tissues (MB, p. 673).

2. If sponge cells are separated, they will regroup. This characteristic is called cell recognition (MB, p. 673)

3. How many layers of cells is a sponge body made up of? Two (MB, p. 673)

4. The flagellated cells that trap food and move water are called choanocytes or collar cells (MB, p. 673).

5. The cells lining the exterior of the sponge are called epidermal cells (IV, Ch. 33.1, Min. 7).

6. The jelly between them is called mesohyl (MB, p. 673). The purpose of the substance is to hold the sponge together and provide a medium for transport (IV, Ch. 33.1, Min. 7).

7. The cells that crawl between the two cell layers are called amoebocytes (MB, p. 674).

8. The purpose of these cells is to carry nutrients and gametes to other cells (MB, p. 674).

9. A simple sponge takes the form of a cylinder with a closed bottom and open top. The hole in the top of the sponge is called the osculum (MB, p. 673) where water flows out of (MB, p. 673) the sponge.

10. The small holes throughout the body of the sponge are called ostia (MB, p. 673) through which water flows into (MB, p. 673) the sponge.

11. How does respiration occur in a sponge?
    By diffusion across cell membranes (IV, Ch. 33.1, Min. 8)

12. How do sponges obtain food?
    The collars on the choanocytes trap plankton as it travels in through the ostia and out through the osculum. (MB, p. 674)

13. Explain both types of asexual reproduction seen in sponges.
    Asexual reproduction occurs by budding when a piece of the sponge breaks off to settle to form a new sponge or by gemmule formation, which occurs in fresh water. Gemmules are internal buds packed with food and amoebocytes. (MB, p. 675)

14. Explain sexual reproduction in sponges.
    Sexual reproduction occurs when an adjacent sponge releases sperm into the water. The sperm travel in through the ostia, are trapped by the collar cells, and transferred to the egg cells by the amoebocytes. The fertilized eggs develop into flagellated larva. (MB, p. 675)

15. Do sponges have gender, or are they hermaphrodites? Hermaphrodites (MB, p. 675)

Phylum Cnidaria

16. What are the two common morphologies seen in cnidarians? __Polyp and medusa (MB, p. 676)__

17. How are these two body shapes specialized with regard to motility of the cnidarian?
    The medusa is specialized for swimming, while the polyp is sessile and cemented to rocks or
    stationary objects. (MB, p. 676)

18. Cnidarians are made up of two tissue layers. The outer layer or covering is called the epidermis (MB, p. 676)

19. The inner layer lining the guts is called the gastrodermis (MB, p. 676).

20. The jellylike substance between the two tissue layers is called mesoglea (MB, p. 676).

21. Cnidarians have a gut called the gastrovascular cavity (MB, p. 676).

22. The cnidarian gut has a single opening, which is significant because __food and waste mix as__
    they both travel into and out of the cavity. (MB, p. 676)

23. Embedded throughout the epidermis and tentacles are specialized cells used for capturing prey and
    defense. These cells are called cnidocytes (MB, p. 677). They contain a specialized harpoonlike
    organelle called a nematocyst (MB, p. 677) What are some specific ways in which these specialized
    cells are used by different species of cnidarians?
    They may be used as harpoons to capture prey, they may inject poison to paralyze prey, or
    they may use them to ward off predators. (MB, p. 677)

24. What are the four different classes of cnidarians?
    Hydrozoa, Scyphozoa, Cubozoa, and Anthozoa (MB, p. 678)

25. What is the dominant morphology of each class?
    Hydrozoans are both dominant polyps and medusa. Scyphozoans and cubozoans are
    dominantly medusa, and anthozoans are dominantly polyps. (MB, pp. 678-681)

26. Describe the nervous system of the cnidarian.
    The nervous system is called a nerve net, which is a loosely connected web of nervous
    system cells that coordinate feeding, movement, and reproduction. (MB, p. 677)

27. Physalia, more specifically the Portuguese man-of-war, belongs to which class? Hydrozoa (MB, p. 678)

28. Hydra live primarily in fresh (MB, p. 679) water.

29. Hydra live symbiotically with certain species of algae (MB, p. 679).

30. Box jellies belong to which class of cnidarians? __Cubozoa (MB, p. 680)__

31. Cup or common jellies belong to which class of cnidarians? Sycphozoa (MB, p. 680)

32. Sea anemones and coral belong to which class of cnidarias? Anthozoa (MB, p. 681)

33. Some species of sea anemones live symbiotically with clownfish. Explain how this relationship benefits both species.

    The anemones provide protection for the clownfish, and the clownfish churn up food and pull

    in plankton for the anemones to feed on. (MB, p. 681)

34. Geographically, where are coral reefs located ?

    Within 30 degrees north and south of the equator (MB, p. 681)

35. What is the base of a coral reef made up of?   Dead polyp skeletons (MB, p. 681)

36. The ciliated larva of a common jelly is called a   planula (MB, p. 680)   .

Phylum Ctenophora

37. Ctenophores are also called comb jellies because of the arrangement of external cilia. How is this cilia arranged, and what is its function?

    The cilia are arranged in eight rows around the organism. The coordinated beating of the cilia

    moves the organism in any direction. (MB, p. 682)

38. The specialized cells located on the tentacles of the ctenophore are called   colloblasts (MB, p. 682)   .

39. The primary function of these cells is to   secrete a sticky substance to attach to prey (MB, p. 682)   .

40. The apical organ is the first suggestion of cephalization. What are its functions?

    It acts to provide position sense to the organism and coordinate the beating of the cilia.

    (MB, p. 682)

Phylum Platyhelminthes

41. What type of symmetry do these animals exhibit?   Bilateral (MB, p. 689)

42. How does their morphology allow them to survive without respiratory and circulatory systems?

    They are very flat so that almost every cell is in contact with a surface for gas and

    nutrient exchange. (MB, p. 689)

43. Flatworms develop from which embryonic tissue layers?

    Ectoderm, endoderm, and mesoderm (MB, p. 689)

44. Describe the nervous system of a flatworm.

    It is arranged as a ladder of cells running down the organism with a concentration of nerve

    cells anteriorly called cerebral ganglia. Some have eyespots that sense light intensity.

    (MB, p. 691)

45. Which pattern of development do these animals undergo?

    They are classed as protostomes even though they are acoelomates. (MB, p. 688)

46. What type of coelom do flatworms have?   They are acoelomates. (MB, p. 689)

47. What are the four classes of flatworms?

Turbellaria, Trematoda, Monogenea, and Cestoda (MB, p. 689)

48. Planarians belong to which class? Turbellaria (MB, p. 690)

49. Describe feeding and digestion in planarians.

They feed on detritus sucked in through the muscular pharynx to the gastrovascular cavity, where the food is broken down. The nutrients diffuse from the cavity out into the tissues. (MB, p. 690)

50. What is the purpose of the excretory system of a flatworm?

To rid the organism of excess osmotic water (MB, p. 690)

51. Describe the excretory system of a flatworm.

The excretory system is made up of flame cells that enclose tufts of beating cilia, which draw in the excess water. The water moves into excretory tubules that end in pore openings on the surface of the organism where the water is expelled. (MB, p. 690)

52. Do these animals exhibit cephalization? How?

Yes. The eyespots and cerebral ganglia are located at the anterior aspect of the organism. (MB, p. 691)

53. When do planarians reproduce asexually? During warm summer weather (MB, p. 691)

54. Briefly explain asexual reproduction in a planarian.

The posterior portion of the flatworm attaches to a stationary surface. It contracts behind its pharynx and pulls forward until it splits into two. Each half regenerates its missing body parts. (MB, p. 691)

55. Parasitic flukes make up which two classes of flatworms? Trematoda and Monogenea (MB, p. 691)

56. What is the difference between an ectoparasite and an endoparasite?

An ectoparasite lives on the surface of another organism, while an endoparasite lives inside the tissues of another organism. (MB, p. 691)

57. How do tapeworms obtain food?

They absorb nutrients through their tegument, or outer covering. (MB, p. 692)

58. The genus Schistosoma is a fluke that requires two very different hosts to complete its life cycle. What organism is the primary host? A human (MB, p. 692)

What organism is the secondary host? A snail (MB, p. 692)

59. How do the schistosomes gain access to these hosts?

Burrowing into the skin (MB, p. 692)

60. All tapeworms belong to which class of flatworm? Cestoda (MB, p. 693)

61. Since tapeworms have no mouth or gastrovascular cavity, how do they obtain nutrition?

They absorb nutrients through their tegument, or outer body covering. (MB, p. 693)

62. The body sections behind the neck of the tapeworm are called proglottids (MB, p. 693).

What do these structures contain? Reproductive structures and fertilized eggs (MB, p. 693)

63. Beef tapeworms are technically named Taenia saginatus (MB, p. 694).

64. Who is the primary host for the beef tapeworm? How does the tapeworm gain access to its primary host?

A human is the primary host. The tapeworm is ingested with undercooked infected beef.

(MB, p. 694)

65. Taenia solium is the tapeworm that uses a pig (MB, p. 694) as an intermediate or secondary host.

Phylum Nematoda

66. Animals classified into this phylum are more commonly known as roundworms (MB, p. 695).

67. Which type of digestive system do nematodes have?

They have a one-way gut tube with two openings. (MB, p. 695)

68. Which type of coelom do they develop? They are pseudocoelomates. (MB, p. 695)

69. What is a cuticle?

An outer covering that protects the worm from the host's immunity (MB, p. 695)

70. The genus Ascaris is a large roundworm that can infect humans, pigs, and horses (MB, p. 696).

71. What do these roundworms eat?

They ingest the food in the intestines of their host. (MB, p. 696)

72. How does a human become infected with this type of roundworm?

They are ingested with contaminated food or water. (MB, p. 696)

73. Hookworms primarily infect cats, dogs, and humans (MB, p. 696).

74. What do hookworms eat?

They feed on blood from the intestinal wall of their host. (MB, p. 696)

75. How does a hookworm gain access to its host?

Some species enter by boring into the bloodstream through the feet, and some enter through

contaminated undercooked meat. (MB, p. 696)

76. Where do hookworm eggs hatch into larva? In the soil (MB, p. 696)

77. Genus Trichinella is a nematode that uses a pig (MB, p. 697) as its primary host.

78. How do humans become infected with a trichina worm?
Eating undercooked pork (MB, p. 697)

79. In which body tissue does this worm choose to spend its larval stage?
Muscles of a pig (MB, p. 697)

80. The disease trichinosis can be fatal if the heart muscle (MB, p. 697) becomes infected.

81. The most common worm infection in the U.S. is enterobius (MB, p. 697) also known as pinworms (MB, p. 697)

82. Who is most affected by these worms? Young children (MB, p. 697)

83. How are the eggs passed from host to host?
Infected children scratch their anus and pick up eggs under their fingernails. They leave the eggs on things they touch, which transfers them to other children. (MB, p. 697)

84. Nematode larva that block lymphatic ducts and cause elephantiasis are called filaria (MB, p. 697).

85. How is this roundworm passed from host to host? A specific mosquito (MB, p. 697)

Phylum Rotifera

86. Rotifers are complex tiny animals inhabiting mostly fresh (MB, p. 698) waters.

87. What do rotifers eat?
Bacteria and protists (MB, p. 698)

88. Describe the digestive system of a rotifer as a piece of food would move through.
The food enters through the mouth and moves into the mastax where it is broken down. From the mastax, it moves into the stomach where it is further digested, then into the intestine where nutrients are absorbed, and finally into the cloaca—a common chamber for waste and gametes. (MB, p. 698)

89. Rotifers have excretory systems that most closely resemble the excretory system of the flatworm (MB, p. 698)

90. What is parthenogenesis, which can be seen in rotifers?
A form of asexual reproduction where a female lays unfertilized eggs that hatch into small females with no genetic variability (MB, p. 698)

91. What is the purpose of the crown of cilia?
The crown of cilia beats food into the mouth. (MB, p. 698)

92. What is the average size of a rotifer?
100-500 μm (MB, p. 698)

CHAPTER 35: Mollusks and Annelids

VOCABULARY

Section 1

1. trochophore:_____

2. visceral mass:_____

3. mantle: _____

4. mantle cavity: _____

5. ganglion:_____

6. radula:_____

7. gastropod:_____

8. hemolymph:_____

9. hemocoel: _____

10. bivalve: _____

11. incurrent siphon: _____

12. excurrent siphon: _____

13. cephalopod: _____

Section 2

14. seta: _____

15. parapodium:_____

SECTION REVIEW KEY

Section 1

1. A true coelom is completely lined by mesoderm, which separates the gut tube from the muscles that move the organism so that digestion and movement do not affect each other. (MB, p. 705)

2. Phyla Mollusca and Annelida (MB, p. 705)

3. The function of the radula of mollusks varies by species. Most mollusks with radula use it to scrape food free and into their mouths. Some species use the radula to bore holes, and a few use their radula as a harpoon. (MB, pp. 706-707)

4. The mantle cavity must remain moist for snail respiration. When the moisture in the air is high, snail tissues receive more oxygen, which accounts for increased activity. (MB, p. 708)

5. Gastropods and bivalves have open circulatory systems, and cephalopods have a closed system. (MB, pp. 707-711)

6. Gastropods move slowly, and most bivalves move very little, so their oxygen needs are low. An open circulatory system is adequate to meet the needs of the organisms. (MB, pp. 707-708)

7. Bivalves (clams) are burrowing animals with a foot to burrow and a hard shell for protection against predators. Cephalopods (squids) are very active predators with developed circulatory and nervous systems, quick reflexes, and strong mantles for propulsion and hunting. (MB, pp. 708-711)

8. They have distinct tops and bottoms, similar right and left sides with eyes, and paired ganglia. (MB, pp. 708-709)

Section 2

1. Each segment may have repeating organs, ensuring survival if part of the organism is damaged. The segmented coelom also allows one part of the organism to move or contract and expand while the rest of the body is unaffected. (MB, p. 713)

2. The earthworm's circular muscle in the middle of the worm contracts first, pushing the anterior end of the worm forward. It anchors its anterior setae and then contracts its longitudinal muscle, pulling the posterior end of the worm forward. (MB, p. 714)

3. An earthworm respires across its tegument. (MB, p. 715)

4. Polychaetes have fleshy feet called parapodia with many bristles extending from them. They have antennae and specialized mouth structures. They are primarily marine and are the only annelids with a trochophore stage. (MB, p. 716)

5. They have suckers at each end for attaching to a host. They feed on blood, secreting an anesthetic so the host does not feel them and an anticoagulant to keep host blood flowing. (MB, p. 716)

Biology Coloring Workbook

Complete Chapter 8: Phylum Annelida, Phylum Mollusca.

16. crop:_____

_____

17. gizzard: _____

_____

18. typhlosole: _____

_____

19. aortic arch: _____

_____

20. nephridium:_____

_____

21. clitellum:_____

_____

22. seminal receptacle: _____

_____

23. chitin: _____

_____

COMPREHENSION QUESTIONS

1. What mollusk/annelid characteristic is thought to make them close relatives? Trochophore (MB, p. 705)

2. Mollusk bodies are divided into two main regions, the __head-foot (MB, p. 706)__ and the __visceral mass (MB, p. 706)__.

3. Which region contains the mouth and sensory structures in a mollusk?
   Head-foot (MB, p. 706)

4. Which region contains the heart, digestive, reproductive, and excretory organs of a mollusk?
   Visceral mass (MB, p. 706)

5. Which mollusk structure produces the hard valves or shells? _____ Mantle (MB, p. 706)

6. Two paired clusters of nerve cells controlling the locomotion, feeding, and sensory processing are located in which regions of the mollusk body?
   The head-foot and the visceral mass (MB, p. 706)

7. A radula might be used to scrape algae, bore holes, cut leaves, and spear prey (MB, pp. 706-707).

8. What is the developmental process called that occurs in gastropods to produce a head that can be retracted?
   Torsion (MB, p. 707)

9. The largest and most diverse class of mollusks is __Gastropoda (MB, p. 707)__.

10. Three examples of gastropods are snails, slugs, conchs, abalones, and nudibranchs (MB, p. 707).

11. What structure of a land snail acts as a modified lung?
    Mantle cavity (MB, p. 706)

12. The marine gastropod that has no shell is the __nudibranch (MB, p. 707)__.

13. Relative to motility, most bivalves are __sessile (MB, p. 709)__.

14. The mantle cavity of a clam is sealed except for two fleshy tubes called __siphons (MB, p. 709)__.

15. Fertilization in clams may occur either __internally (MB, p. 709)__ or __externally (MB, p. 710)__.

16. What type of feeding do most cephalopods exhibit? __Predatory carnivores (MB, p. 710)__

17. What are the main characteristics of the nervous system of a cephalopod?
    High degree of cephalization with complex nervous systems (MB, p. 710)

18. What are the specialized pigment cells which allow a cephalopod to blend with its environment?
    Chromatophores (MB, p. 711)

19. A squid usually has __two__ tentacle(s) specialized for preying on and capturing food and __ten__ total.
    (MB, p. 711)

20. Architeuthis is the largest invertebrate. What is it? __Giant squid (MB, p. 711)__

21. The chambered nautilus discharges water from the chambers of its shell for what purpose?
    It uses this to control buoyancy. It fills the chamber with gas when it wants to rise and water
    to sink. (MB, p. 711)

22. The segmented coelom of the earthworm allows for muscle contraction and movement without
    affecting _____ digestion and metabolic processes (MB, p. 713) _____.

23. The most commonly known oligochaete is the __earthworm (MB, p. 713)__.

24. Contraction of which muscle in the earthworm causes the initial increase in pressure of the coelomic
    fluid in the first stage of locomotion?
    The circular muscle (MB, p. 714)

25. What are the two main circulatory structures in the earthworm responsible for pumping blood?
    The aortic arches and the dorsal blood vessel (MB, p. 715)

26. An annelid is equipped with an excretory system to eliminate excess water. What are the main organs of
    this system?
    Nephridia (MB, p. 715)

27. What is the clitellum is responsible for?
    It is responsible for secreting mucus to pick up sperm and forming a thick protective case for
    the baby worms to develop after the eggs have been fertilized. (MB, pp. 715-716)

28. The largest class of annelids is the class __Polychaeta (MB, p. 716)__.

29. Leeches belong to which class of annelids? __Hirudinea (MB, p. 716)__

30. Leeches secrete both an __anesthetic (MB, p. 716)__ so their host cannot feel them and an
    __anticoagulant (MB, p. 716)__ to keep blood from clotting.

31. The majority of polychaetes live in __the ocean (MB, p. 716)__

32. Put the digestive organs of the earthworm in order as food passes through them.

Anus	Crop	Esophagus	Gizzard	Intestine	Mouth	Pharynx

a. Mouth (MB, p. 714)

b. Pharynx (MB, p. 714)

c. Esophagus (MB, p. 714)

d. Crop (MB, p. 714)

e. Gizzard (MB, p. 714)

f. Intestine (MB, p. 714)

g. Anus (MB, p. 714)

Label the diagrams of the earthworm. (BCW, p. 237) (MB, p. 714)

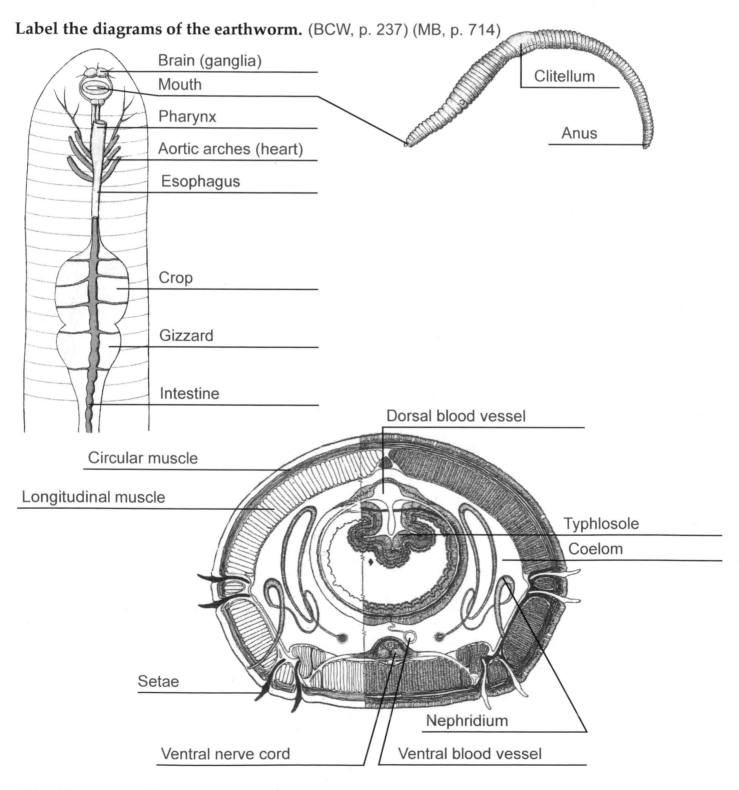

Brain (ganglia)

Mouth

Pharynx

Aortic arches (heart)

Esophagus

Crop

Gizzard

Intestine

Clitellum

Anus

Circular muscle

Longitudinal muscle

Dorsal blood vessel

Typhlosole

Coelom

Setae

Nephridium

Ventral nerve cord

Ventral blood vessel

Label the diagram of the clam. (BCW, p. 239)

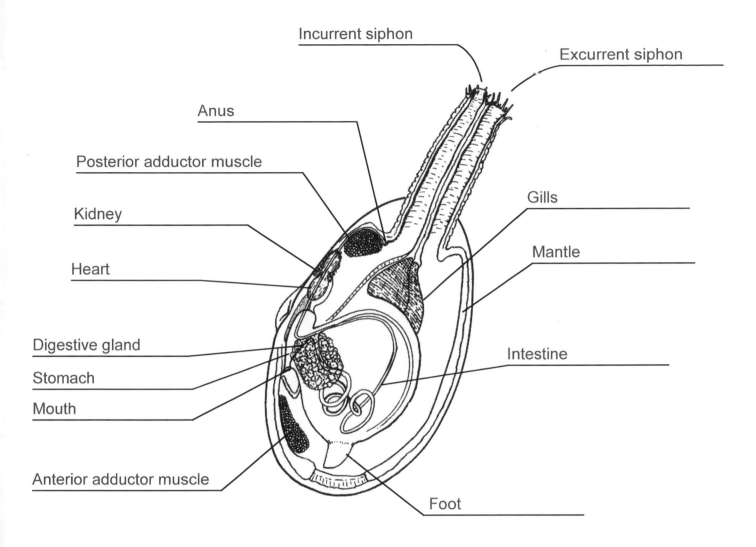

Incurrent siphon

Excurrent siphon

Anus

Posterior adductor muscle

Gills

Kidney

Mantle

Heart

Digestive gland

Intestine

Stomach

Mouth

Anterior adductor muscle

Foot

SECTION REVIEW KEY

Chapter 36, Section 1

1. Arthropods are characterized by segmented bodies and jointed appendages. They are also all coelomates, have exoskeletons, and have open circulatory systems. (MB, p. 723)

2. The outer layer of the exoskeleton is protective in that it is waterproof, helps the animal conserve water, and keeps it from drying out. The middle layer is protective. The inner layer gives the exoskeleton some flexibility and reduces friction at the joints. (MB, p. 723)

3. Compound eyes are made up of multiple light sensors, each with its own lens for light refraction. (MB, p. 723)

4. Molting is the shedding of an exoskeleton and the growth of a new one. (MB, p. 724)

5. Chelicerae are pincerlike mouthparts, and mandibles are jawlike mouthparts. (MB, p. 724)

6. Trilobita: extinct trilobites
   Chelicerata: ticks, mites, horseshoe crabs, scorpions
   Crustacea: shrimp, crabs, lobsters, water fleas, barnacles
   Myriapoda: centipedes and millipedes
   Hexapoda: insects (MB, p. 725)

7. The layers may function differently according to the needs of the specific species of arthropod. (MB, p. 723)

Chapter 36, Section 2

1. Crustaceans have characteristic paired appendages, two pairs of antennae, and nauplius larvae. (MB, p. 726)

2. Copepods are abundant in plankton and make up the base of all marine food chains. (MB, p. 727)

3. Chelipeds are used to capture food, while the mandibles are used for chewing food. (MB, p. 728)

4. As a crayfish walks, it moves water across the gills for gas exchange. (MB, p. 729)

Chapter 36, Section 3

1. Arachnids are characterized by their two body segments: the abdomen and the cephalothorax with six pairs of jointed appendages. (MB, pp. 731-732)

2. Pedipalps function primarily to hold and manipulate food. (MB, p. 731)

3. Spiders spin sticky webs to catch prey and may bind them in the silk for storage. Some spiders are venomous. (MB, pp. 732-733)

VOCABULARY

Chapter 36, Section 1

1. arthropod:_____

2. appendage:_____

3. chitin: _____

4. compound eye: _____

5. molting:_____

6. trilobite: _____

7. tagma: _____

8. mandible: _____

9. chelicera:_____

Chapter 36, Section 2

10. nauplius:_____

11. cirrus:_____

12. isopod:_____

13. decapod: _____

14. cephalothorax:_____

15. thorax: _____

---

4. Scorpions have stingers at the base of the abdomen, while spiders do not. Scorpions also have large pincer pedipalps for hunting prey. (MB, p. 733)

5. Ticks are all parasitic, while mites live freely. (MB, p. 733)

6. Millipedes are slow movers, are herbivorous, and have rounded bodies with two appendages on each segment. Centipedes are fast movers, are carnivorous, and have flattened bodies with one appendage on each body segment. (MB, p. 734)

Chapter 37, Section 1

1. Small size, wings, and relatively short life span have made insects successful in a variety of habitats. (MB, p. 742)

2. Insects harm society by eating crops and wood and acting as vectors for disease transmission. They benefit society by pollinating plants and recycling nutrients to the soil. (MB, p. 744)

3. [Skip]

16. carapace: _____

17. abdomen: _____

18. antenna: _____

19. antennule: _____

20. cheliped: _____

21. swimmeret: _____

22. telson: _____

23. uropod: _____

24. digestive gland: _____

25. green gland: _____

Chapter 36, Section 3

26. arachnid: _____

27. pedipalp: _____

28. spinneret: _____

29. book lung: _____

30. trachea: _____

31. spiracle: _____

32. Malpighian tubule: _____

4. Complete metamorphosis involves an egg hatching into a larva, which has a different niche than its adult form. Incomplete metamorphosis involves an egg hatching into a nymph, which is a small immature version of its adult form. (MB, p. 748)

5. Batesian mimicry involves harmless insects imitating dangerous insects. Mullerian mimicry involves harmful insects imitating another species. (MB, p. 750)

6. [Skip]

7. Hormones (MB, pp. 748-749)

8. Batesian (MB, p. 750)

Chapter 37, Section 2

1. Pheromones: ant trails and hive identification
   Sounds: crickets chirp and mosquitoes buzz to attract mates
   Lights: lightning bugs flash to identify themselves and attract mates
   (MB, pp. 751-752)

2. The queen must be fed royal jelly while it is developing. (MB, p. 753)

3. The queen moves to a new hive and takes half of the workers with her. (MB, p. 753)

4. They perform different movements called dances, which tell the other bees the direction the food is in or how far away the food is. (MB, pp. 753-754)

5. Expose the bees to pheromones they cannot see and observe their behavior. (MB, pp. 751-752)

6. Innate behavior in bees contributes to their success as a species because it allows them to put the safety and welfare of the hive or queen ahead of their own lives. (MB, pp. 752, 754)

7. Mating with a drone from a different hive would bring genetic variability to the colony, which would make the colony stronger. (MB, p. 753)

Chapter 38, Section 1

1. Echinoderms are characterized by pentaradial symmetry and their water-vascular system with tube feet. (MB, p. 761)

2. Crinoidea: sea lilies and feather stars
   Ophiuroidea: basket stars and brittle stars
   Echinoidea: sea urchins and sand dollars
   Holothuroidea: sea cucumbers
   Asteroidea: sea stars (MB, pp. 762-764)

3. Muscles surrounding a small bulblike structure called an ampulla contract and force water into the tube feet, extending them. Muscles in the tube feet contract and force water back into the ampulla, retracting the feet. (MB, p. 666)

4. Any part of the sea star body can regenerate a new body as long as specific portions of the nerves remain intact. Sea stars may also split in half, with each half regenerating the lost half. (MB, p. 767)

5. Sea urchins are deuterostomes and exhibit the developmental processes of deuterostomes. Mollusks are protostomes and exhibit the developmental processes of protostomes. (MB, pp. 705, 761)

6. Tube feet are used for movement and to capture prey. Without the water in the water-vascular system, the feet would be ineffective at both. (MB, p. 766)

Chapter 38, Section 2

1. Chordates are characterized by a notochord, a dorsal nerve cord, pharyngeal pouches, and a postanal tail. (MB, p. 768)

2. Pharyngeal pouches were originally used as filter feeding mechanisms, and it is thought they later developed into gills. (MB, p. 769)

3. Segmented muscles (MB, p. 770)

4. Enlarged pharynx (MB, p. 770)

Biology Coloring Workbook

Complete Chapter 8: Phylum Arthropoda, Phylum Echinodermata.

Chapter 37, Section 1

33. **entomology:** _____

_____

34. **labrum:** _____

_____

35. **labium:** _____

_____

36. **tympanum:** _____

_____

37. **ovipositor:** _____

_____

38. **metamorphosis:** _____

_____

39. **incomplete metamorphosis:** _____

_____

40. **nymph:** _____

_____

41. **complete metamorphosis:** _____

_____

42. **pupa:** _____

_____

Chapter 37, Section 2

43. **pheromone:** _____

_____

44. **social insect:** _____

_____

45. **innate behavior:** _____

_____

46. **worker bee:** _____

_____

47. **queen bee:** _____

_____

48. **drone:** _____

_____

49. **royal jelly:** _____

_____

50. queen factor: _____

_____

51. altruistic behavior: _____

_____

52. kin selection: _____

Chapter 38, Section 1

53. echinoderm: _____

_____

54. ossicle:_____

_____

55. water-vascular system:_____

_____

56. tube foot: _____

_____

57. test:_____

_____

58. pedicellaria: _____

_____

59. madreporite:_____

_____

60. stone canal:_____

_____

61. ring canal:_____

_____

62. radial canal: _____

_____

63. ampulla: _____

_____

64. cardiac stomach: _____

_____

65. pyloric stomach: _____

_____

66. bipinnaria: _____

Chapter 38, Section 2

67. atriopore: _____

_____

COMPREHENSION QUESTIONS

Phylum Arthropoda

1. List four animals that belong to the phylum Arthropoda.
   Crabs, insects, scorpions, barnacles (any four) (MB, p. 725)

2. What three characteristics distinguish arthropods from other animals?
   Segmented bodies, jointed appendages, and an exoskeleton (MB, p. 723)

3. List three different examples of jointed appendages seen in arthropods.
   Feet and legs, antennae, and chelipeds or maxillipeds (MB, p. 728)

4. What is an exoskeleton made up of?
   The waxy outer layer is protein and fat. The middle layer is protein and a tough polysaccharide called chitin. The innermost layer is made up of protein and a more flexible chitin. (MB, p. 723)

5. Which part of the animal secretes or produces the exoskeleton?
   The epidermis (MB, p. 723)

6. Describe one advantage and one disadvantage of an exoskeleton.
   One advantage is the exoskeleton makes the animal very hard to eat, so predators must be very determined. One disadvantage is that it does not grow with the animal, so it must be shed and rebuilt. This leaves the animal very vulnerable while it is producing a new exoskeleton. (MB, pp. 723-724)

7. Describe cephalization in arthropods.
   They have complex eyes and sensory structures located anteriorly, with a brain connected to a ventral nerve cord for coordination. (MB, p. 723)

8. What type of circulatory system is seen in arthropods? Open (MB, p. 723)

9. Into what five subphyla are arthropods divided? Give an example of an animal from each.
   a. Trilobita: Extinct trilobites (MB, p. 725)
   b. Chelicerata: Horseshoe crabs, ticks, mites, spiders, and scorpions (MB, p. 725)
   c. Crustacea: Shrimp, copepods, barnacles, crabs, lobsters, pill bugs, and sea lice (MB, p. 725)
   d. Myriapoda: Centipedes and millipedes (MB, p. 725)
   e. Hexapoda: Insects (MB, p. 725)

10. On what basis are arthropods placed into a specific subphylum? Their appendages (MB, p. 724)

11. What is a tagma? A structure composed of several fused body segments (MB, p. 724)

12. What is the difference between an arthropod's mandibles and its chelicerae?
    Mandibles are jawlike structures making up the mouth. Chelicerae are pincers used to manipulate food or objects. (MB, p. 724)

13. Most crustaceans have 16-20 body segments that are fused into several ___tagmata (MB, p. 726)___ .

14. How do crustaceans respire?

They may respire through a thin area of exoskeleton if they are terrestrial or through gills if they are aquatic. (MB, p. 726)

15. What is a nauplius?

An embryo that hatches into a free-swimming larva with a single eye and three pairs of appendages. After several molts, it will take on its adult form. (MB, p. 726)

16. What are the primary differences between isopods, copepods, and decapods?

Isopods are small terrestrial crustaceans that include pill bugs. Copepods are small aquatic organisms that make up plankton. Decapods are larger aquatic crustaceans such as crayfish, lobster, crab, and shrimp. (MB, pp. 727-728)

17. Label the external structures of the crayfish, and briefly describe the function of each.

  a. Abdomen: One tagma containing the viscera (MB, p. 728)

  b. Cephalothorax: Two tagma (head and thorax) covered by the hard carapace (shell) (MB, p. 728)

  c. Compound eye: Detects light (MB, pp. 729-730)

  d. Appendages (one set attached to each segment):

  1. Antennae and antennules: Sensory structures (MB, p. 728)

  2. Mandibles: Chewing food (MB, p. 728)

  3. Maxilla or maxillipeds: Sensory organs, manipulate food (MB, p. 728)

  4. Walking legs and swimmerets: Locomotion and sperm transfer (MB, p. 728)

  5. Chelipeds: Pincers for hunting and defense (MB, p. 728)

  6. Tail made up of telson and uropods: Locomotion (MB, p. 729)

(MB, pp. 728-729)

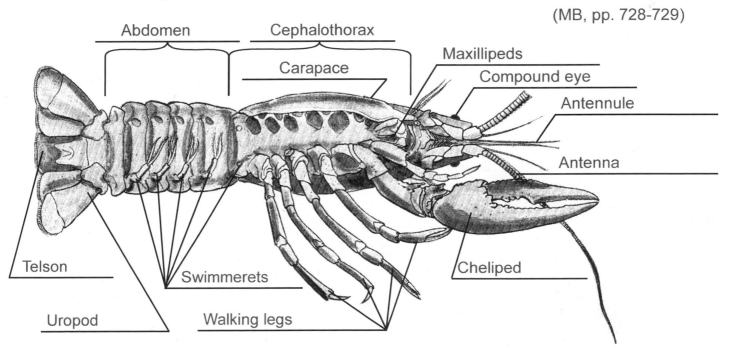

18. Briefly describe the function of each internal crayfish organ. Refer to Diagram 36-8 in the text.
    a. Digestive gland: ___Secretes digestive enzymes into the stomach (MB, p. 729)___
    b. Stomach: ___Organ that contains small teeth to grind food into paste (MB, p. 729)___
    c. Gills: ___Function in gas exchange and are contained within each walking leg (MB, p. 729)___
    d. Heart: ___Pumps hemolymph into large vessels (MB, p. 729)___
    e. Green glands: ___Excretory organs that function in waste and water elimination (MB, p. 730)___
    f. Ventral nerve cord: ___Carries nerve impulses from the cerebral ganglia (MB, p. 730)___

19. Why do terrestrial crustaceans live in moist dark environments?
    They lack structures that are adapted for water conservation and must keep their bodies moist.
    (MB, p. 727)

20. Which groups of organisms are classed into the subphylum Chelicerata?
    Spiders and scorpions. Also mites, ticks, chiggers, sea spiders, and horseshoe crabs.
    (MB, p. 731)

21. Why are these animals placed into this subphylum?
    Because they have chelicerae (MB, p. 731)

22. What are chelicerae?
    The first pair of appendages, which are either fangs or pincers (MB, p. 731)

23. Label the external structures of the spider, and briefly describe the function of each.
    a. Cephalothorax: ___Most anterior tagma with six pairs of appendages (MB, p. 731)___
    b. Abdomen: ___Posterior tagma containing most of the viscera (MB, pp. 731-732)___
    c. Chelicerae: ___Modified fangs for injecting venom into prey (MB, p. 732)___
    d. Pedipalps: ___Aid in manipulating food (MB, p. 731)___
    e. Simple eyes: ___Most have eight at the anterior aspect of the cephalothorax (MB, p. 732)___
    f. Spinnerets: ___Tubes that connect to silk glands in the abdomen (MB, p. 732)___

(MB, p. 731) Pedipalp

Chelicerae

Cephalothorax

Walking leg

Simple eyes

Abdomen

Spinneret

24. Briefly describe the function of each internal spider organ. Refer to Figure 36-9 in the text.
   a. Book lungs: _Folded, paired sacs modified for respiration on land (MB, p. 732)_
   b. Poison gland: _Produces venom that is transferred to the chelicerae (MB, p. 732)_
   c. Malpighian tubes: _Excretory tubules for waste and water conservation (MB, p. 732)_
   d. Sucking stomach: _Digestive organ used in the breakdown of food (MB, p. 731)_
   e. Digestive gland: _Secretes digestive enzymes into the stomach (MB, p. 731)_
   f. Heart: _Pumps into several large vessels and then into an open coelom (MB, p. 731)_
   g. Silk glands: _Produce the protein used for the spider web (MB, p. 732)_

25. Which two spiders found in the U.S. have venom dangerous to humans?
   Black widow and brown recluse (MB, p. 732)

26. What two common diseases are caused by the bite of an infected tick?
   Lyme disease and Rocky Mountain spotted fever (MB, p. 733)

27. Are scorpion babies hatched from eggs or born live? In what significant way does the scorpion mother tend to her young?
   They are born live and ride on their mother's back for 1-2 weeks following their birth.
   (IV, Chapter 36.3, Minute 7)

28. Which two main classes of organisms belong to the subphylum Myriapoda?
   Centipedes and millipedes (MB, p. 734)

29. What are the names of the two classes respectively?
   Centipedes belong to the class Chilopoda, and millipedes belong to the class Diplopoda.
   (MB, p. 734)

30. Compare and contrast the major distinguishing characteristics between centipedes and millipedes.

Centipedes	Millipedes
One pair of long unbranched antennae	One pair of short branched antennae
One pair of long legs on each body segment	Two pairs of short legs on each body segment
Long flattened bodies	Rounded bodies with up to 100 segments
Fast moving	Slow moving
Predators with poison claws	Eat plants or detritus
Live in damp dark areas	Live in damp dark areas (MB, p. 734)

31. Insects are all placed into the subphylum called _Hexapoda (MB, p. 741)_.

32. Approximately how many species of insects have been identified and classified? _One million (MB, p. 742)_

33. What single characteristic makes insects so successful as a species? _They can fly. (MB, p. 742)_

34. How many distinct tagmata do insects have?
   Three: head, thorax, and abdomen (MB, p. 741)

35. How many pairs of appendages do insects have?

Three pairs of legs and one or two sets of wings (MB, p. 741)

36. Why are insects a vital part of all terrestrial and freshwater ecosystems?

They are a primary food source to most fish and birds and some animals. They pollinate

flowers and plants; they produce honey, wax, and silk; and they are natural nutrient recyclers.

(MB, p. 744)

37. Refer to Table 37-1 (Common Insect Orders) in the text, and fill in one or two examples of insects for each order. (MB, p. 743)

a. Hemiptera: _____True bugs such as stinkbugs or bedbugs_____

b. Homoptera: _____Aphids, mealy bugs, and cicadas_____

c. Isoptera: _____Termites_____

d. Odonata: _____Dragonflies and damselflies_____

e. Orthoptera: _____Grasshoppers, crickets, and katydids_____

f. Coleoptera: _____Weevils, ladybugs, and beetles_____

g. Diptera: _____Mosquitoes, flies, and gnats_____

h. Hymenoptera: _____Bees, wasps, and ants_____

i. Lepidoptera: _____Butterflies and moths_____

38. Label the external structures of the grasshopper, and give a brief description of the function of each.

a. Head: The anterior part of an insect body with eyes, antennae, and mouthparts (MB, p. 745)

b. Thorax: The body section after the head, with the legs and wings attached (MB, p. 745)

Into what three sections is the thorax divided? Prothorax, mesothorax, metathorax (MB, p. 745)

c. Abdomen: The posterior section of the body containing the reproductive and digestive organs (MB, pp. 745-746)

d. Spiracles: Pores for gas exchange (MB, p. 746)

e. Walking legs: Two sets of legs used to walk (MB, p. 745)

f. Jumping legs: One set of legs used to jump (MB, p. 745)

g. Wings: Outgrowths of the body wall that enable insects to fly. There are usually two sets, forewings and hindwings. (MB, p. 745)

h. Ovipositors: Seen in females and used to dig holes for laying fertilized eggs (MB, p. 748)

i. Simple and compound eyes: Three sets of simple eyes sense light intensity, while compound eyes sense movement and can form images. (MB, p. 747)

j. Tympanum (not on diagram): Oval membrane and cavity in the abdomen for sensing sound (MB, p. 747)

k. Antenna: Sensory structures that respond to touch and smell (MB, p. 747)

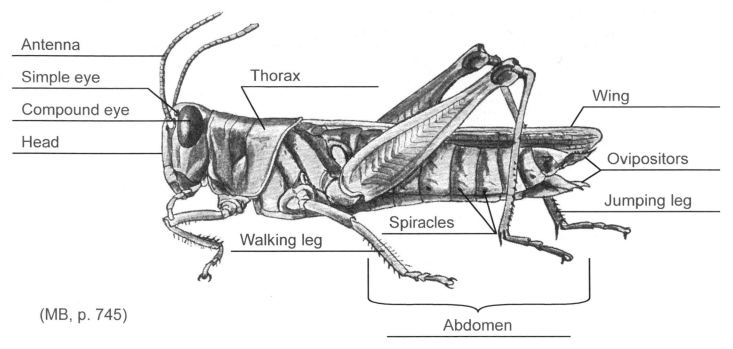

Antenna
Simple eye
Compound eye
Head
Thorax
Wing
Ovipositors
Jumping leg
Spiracles
Walking leg
Abdomen

(MB, p. 745)

39. List the structures involved in grasshopper feeding and digestion in order from ingestion to excretion.

Mouth (mandible and maxilla), esophagus, crop, gizzard, midgut, hindgut, anus (MB, p. 746)

40. How does gas exchange occur in the grasshopper?

Air enters through the spiracles on the thorax and abdomen. The air enters the trachea, which consist of a complex network of tubules that reach all of the cells. Oxygen diffuses in, while carbon dioxide diffuses out of the cells. (MB, pp. 746-747)

41. All insects begin life as an egg and undergo several molts before they reach maturity. How is incomplete metamorphosis different from complete metamorphosis?

With regard to incomplete metamorphosis, the insect egg hatches into a nymph that lacks wings and has undeveloped reproductive capability. After several molts, it reaches its mature adult morphology. With regard to complete metamorphosis, the insect egg hatches into a larva—a wormlike caterpillar that eats and grows until it is mature. It then hangs upside down, gets shorter and fatter until it splits its exoskeleton, and forms a chrysalis or a cocoon where it will molt into a sexually mature winged insect. (MB, pp. 748-749)

42. What are the advantages of metamorphosis?

Reduces competition for resources between the juvenile and adult forms of the insect. It also allows the insect to hibernate during cold weather. (MB, p. 749)

43. What is passive insect defense?

Coloring or camouflage that discourages predators (MB, p. 750)

44. What is Mullerian mimicry?

When a harmful insect's coloring mimics another harmful insect's coloring (MB, p. 750)

45. What is Batesian mimicry?

When a harmless insect's coloring mimics a dangerous insect's coloring (MB, p. 750)

46. What are two types of active insect defense?

Venomous stingers or noxious spray (MB, p. 750)

47. In what ways do insects communicate with each other?

Pheromones, sounds, and lights (MB, pp. 751-752)

48. Honeybees are social insects living in complex colonies with social divisions. What are the three social divisions in bee colonies, and what are their primary functions?

a. Worker bees: Nonreproducing females that perform all the duties of the hive (MB, p. 752)

b. Drone bees: Develop from unfertilized eggs and deliver sperm to the queen (MB, p. 752)

c. Queen: Functions only to reproduce and lays thousands of eggs each year (MB, p. 752)

49. What are the primary jobs of the worker bees?

Secrete wax to build the hive; protect the hive, clean the hive, and circulate air through the hive; secrete royal jelly for the queen; gather nectar and pollen to feed the larva, drones, and queen; kill the drones at the end of the season when food becomes scarce (MB, pp. 752-753)

50. What are the "dances of the bees"?

Patterns of movement that communicate the location of a food source (MB, pp. 753-754)

51. What different messages do the round and waggle dances communicate?

The round dance communicates that a food source is near the hive but not its exact location. The waggle dance communicates that food is far from the hive and its specific location. (MB, pp. 753-754)

52. What is altruistic behavior exhibited in bees?

Genetic traits passed on through the queen to cause all worker bees to save the queen for the life of the hive. Worker bees sacrifice their own lives anytime they sting an intruder or predator to the hive. (MB, p. 754)

Phylum Echinodermata and Invertebrate Chordates

53. What are some examples of animals that are classed as echinoderms?

Sea stars, sea urchins, sand dollars, and sea cucumbers (MB, p. 761)

54. What type of symmetry do most echinoderms exhibit?

Radial or pentaradial (MB, p. 761)

55. What is their common habitat?

Marine waters that range from very shallow to very deep (MB, p. 761)

56. What pattern of development do echinoderms undergo?

They are deutcrostomes. (MB, p. 761)

57. Echinoderms are further classified into six major classes. List the five classes we've discussed and one or two examples from each class.

a. Crinoidea: Sea lilies and feather stars (Fig. 38-2) (MB, p. 762)

b. Ophiuroidea: Basket stars and brittle stars (Fig. 38-3) (MB, p. 763)

c. Echinoidea: Sea urchins and sand dollars (Fig. 38-4) (MB, p. 763)

d. Holothuroidea: Sea cucumbers (Fig. 38-5) (MB, p. 764)

e. Asteroidea: Sea stars (Fig. 38-6) (MB, p. 764)

58. How does gas exchange occur in an echinoderm?

Skin gills are pores on the surface of the organism that lead to hollow tubes for water to flow in. Oxygen and carbon dioxide diffuse from the water into the tissues from the open coelom. (MB, p. 766)

59. What do sea stars and other echinoderms eat?

Slower-moving animals such as mollusks and worms (MB, p. 766)

60. Explain the echinoderm digestive structures and functions.

The sea star pushes its cardiac stomach out through the esophagus and mouth into a bivalve where the soft organism is engulfed, partially digested, and pulled back in through the mouth and esophagus. The food is transferred to the pyloric stomach where enzymes from the digestive glands in each arm finish breaking down the food. The nutrients are absorbed through the coelom, and then waste is expelled through the anus on the aboral side of the sea star. (MB, p. 766)

61. What is the water-vascular system seen in echinoderms?

A network of water-filled canals connected to tube feet that allow the sea star to withdraw and extend its feet for movement (MB, p. 766)

62. Briefly describe the structures of the water-vascular system below. Refer to Figure 38-7 in the text.

a. Madreporite: Sievelike plate opening on the aboral surface that allows water to flow into the system (MB, pp. 765-766)

b. Stone canal: Hollow tube connecting the madreporite to the ring canal (MB, pp. 765-766)

c. Ring canal: Circular hollow tube that connects the stone canal to the radial canals (MB, pp. 765-766)

d. Radial canals: Hollow tubes that extend from the ring canal down each arm of the organism (MB, pp. 765-766)

e. Ampulla:___Muscular, bulblike sac at the upper end of each tube foot (MB, pp. 765-766)___

f. Tube feet:___Thousands of tiny muscular tubes of water that extend out of every arm___
       (MB, pp. 765-766)

63. Explain how the water-vascular system produces locomotion in echinoderms.
    Water flows in through the madreporite and proceeds through the canals to the ampulla.
    Muscles around the ampulla contract, pushing water into the tube feet and causing them
    to extend. Muscles in the tube feet contract to push the water back up into the ampulla,
    retracting the tube feet. (MB, p. 766)

64. Describe the nervous system and sensory structures of a sea star.
    Echinoderms have no brain but a nerve ring that forms a circle around the mouth of the sea
    star. Radial nerves branch from the nerve ring and extend down each arm. These nerves
    coordinate the movement of the tube feet, pedicellariae, spines, and skin gills. They are also
    connected to the eyespots at the end of each arm. (MB, pp. 766-767)

65. What are the bilaterally symmetrical echinoderm larva called? ___Bipinnaria (MB, p. 767)___

66. Where does fertilization occur with regard to echinoderms?
    Externally as both eggs and sperm are shed into the water (MB, p. 767)

67. Label the starfish below. (MB, p. 765)

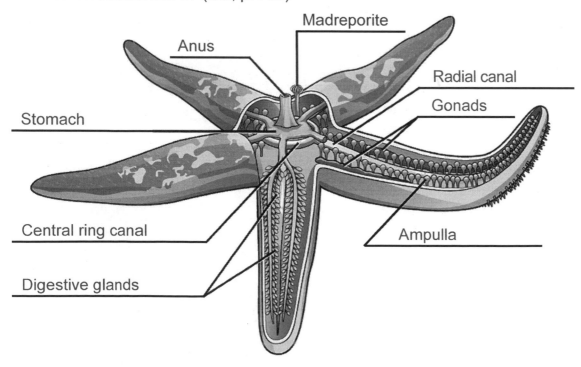

Invertebrate Chordates: Phylum Chordata

68. What are the two subphyla of invertebrate chordates? Give an organismal example for each.

a. ___Cephalochordata: Lancelets (MB, p. 769)___

b. ___Urochordata: Tunicates (MB, p. 769)___

69. What three physical structures must be present at some point in an animal's life to be classified as a chordate?
___A dorsal nerve cord, pharyngeal pouches, and a postanal tail (MB, p. 768)___

70. What is a notochord?
___A stiff but flexible rod of tissue running along the dorsal surface of the animal (MB, p. 768)___

71. What are pharyngeal pouches?
___Pockets in the pharynx that make up the digestive tract between the mouth and the___
___esophagus. They will develop into gills in aquatic chordates and into jaws, inner ear, or___
___miscellaneous organs in terrestrial chordates. (MB, p. 769)___

72. What is a postanal tail?
___A tail that extends past the anus to the end of the dorsal nerve cord (MB, p. 769)___

73. Where do lancelets live?
___They burrow into the sand of warm, shallow marine waters. (MB, p. 770)___

74. What are tunicates?
___Sessile, barrel-shaped animals living on the ocean floor (MB, p. 770)___

75. Why are they called tunicates?
___Their bodies are covered in a tough outer tunic. (MB, p. 770)___

76. What is the most common, well-known tunicate?
___Sea squirt (MB, p. 770)___

77. Refer to Figure 38-12 in the text. The adult tunicate is a very simple squishy growth on the ocean floor and has very simple morphology. Why are these organisms classed in the phylum Chordata?
___In their juvenile form, they possess a notochord, pharyngeal pouches, and a postanal tail.___
___(MB, p. 770)___

APPENDIX

PARTS OF A MICROSCOPE

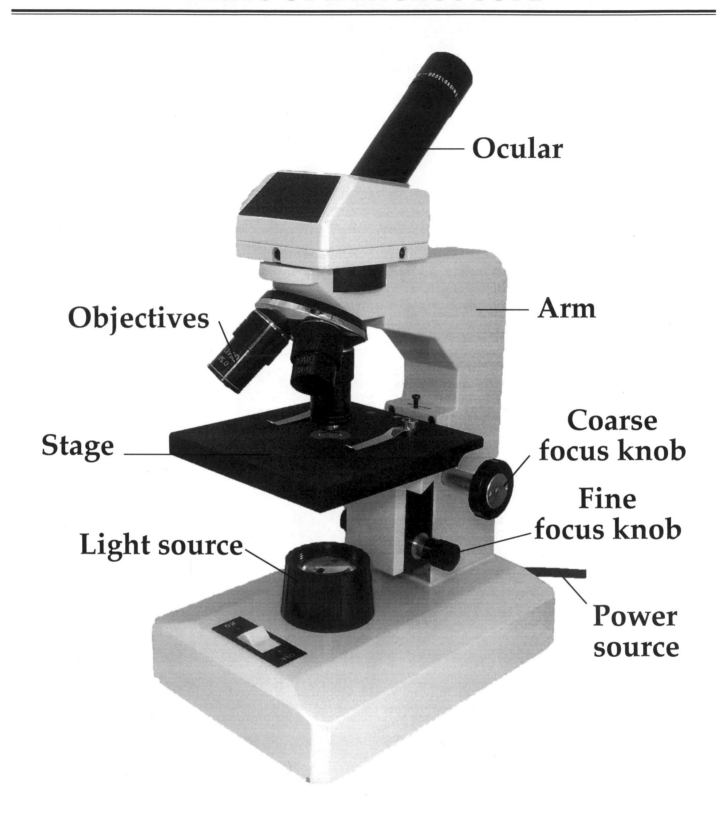

Ocular

Arm

Objectives

Coarse
focus knob

Stage

Fine
focus knob

Light source

Power
source

IMAGE CREDITS

Unless noted below, images are in the public domain.

CHAPTER 1

"Vintage Swift Model M3200 Professional Student Series Microscope With Turret Lenses (10x, 25x & 65x) And Light Source, Made In Japan" by Joe Haupt (https://flic.kr/p/FXaXds). License: CC BY 2.0

CHAPTER 3

Protein structures by CNX OpenStax Anatomy and Physiology (https://bit.ly/2myqnyW). License: CC BY 4.0

Cell membrane detailed diagram by Dhatfield (https://bit.ly/2LOljBd). License: CC BY-SA 3.0

DNA nucleotides by CNX OpenStax Anatomy and Physiology (https://bit.ly/2Oaiex0). License: CC BY 4.0

CHAPTER 4

"Cell nucleus diagram" by Chippolito (https://bit.ly/2LH0jzw). License: CC BY-SA 3.0

CHAPTER 8

"Mitosis vs. Meiosis" by Community College Consortium for Bioscience Credentials (https://bit.ly/2vpdpZ2). License: CC BY 3.0

CHAPTER 24

"Structure of a enveloped helical virus" by Anderson Brito (https://bit.ly/2BlwgK5). License: CC BY-SA 3.0

"A simplified 3D-generated structure of the adenovirus" by Thomas Splettstoesser (https://bit.ly/2PfVcW5). License: CC BY-SA 4.0

CHAPTER 25

"Amoeba" by Kupirijo (https://bit.ly/2waFlzm). License: CC BY-SA 3.0

"Euglena Anatomy Diagram" by Chillery16 (https://bit.ly/2tPU1oF). License: CC BY-SA 3.0

CHAPTER 29

"A diagram of a highly idealized eudicot" by Kelvinsong (https://bit.ly/2LdWAW5). License: CC BY-SA 3.0

CHAPTER 32

"Proto vs. Deuterostomes" by Yassine Mrabet (https://bit.ly/2PMahyY). License: CC BY-SA 3.0

CHAPTER 33 & 34

"Sea Sponge Diagram" by Kelvinsong (https://bit.ly/2ww5M2R). License: CC BY-SA 3.0

"Schematic drawing of the anatomy of Dugesia gonocephala" by Andreas Neudecker (https://bit.ly/2okM860). License: CC BY-SA 3.0

LICENSE INFORMATION

CC BY 2.0	Creative Commons Attribution 2.0 Generic (https://bit.ly/1ryPA8o)
CC BY 3.0	Creative Commons Attribution 3.0 Unported (https://bit.ly/1E6HPMf)
CC BY-SA 3.0	Creative Commons Attribution-ShareAlike 3.0 Unported (https://bit.ly/1p2b8Ke)
CC BY 4.0	Creative Commons Attribution 4.0 International (https://bit.ly/2f0aOjs)
CC BY-SA 4.0	Creative Commons Attribution-ShareAlike 4.0 International (https://bit.ly/1xMszCg)

TEST KEY

CHAPTER 1 TEST: The Science of Life

Name:_____ Date: _____ Score: _____

Circle the best answer.

1. Biology is
   a. The study of zoology
   b. The study of epidemiology
   c. The study of life
   d. The study of the twilight zone

2. Walking into a dark room causes the pupils in your eyes to immediately dilate. This example best describes which of the characteristics of life?
   a. Reproduction
   b. Growth and development
   c. Adaptability and change over time
   d. Responding to stimuli

3. Living things increase in size by
   a. Cell differentiation
   b. Growth and reproduction
   c. Responding to stimuli
   d. DNA transfer from one cell to another

4. An example of metabolism is
   a. The organelles of a kidney cell all working together to maintain a constant blood pressure
   b. Converting a spaghetti dinner into usable energy to run a race
   c. The ability of an organism to reproduce an identical organism
   d. The fifth toe on your foot growing smaller with consecutive generations due to lack of use

5. Homeostasis is
   a. The sum of the processes of an organism to transform matter into energy
   b. Populations undergoing genetic adaptations over time
   c. The degree of order of an organism's internal and external parts
   d. The ability of an organism to maintain stable internal conditions when external conditions change.

Answer the following question.

6. All living organisms show some degree of order or organization. What is the smallest functional unit that exhibits all of the characteristics of life and order? _____Cell_____

List below the seven characteristics all living organisms exhibit.

7. Cells and organization

8. Metabolism

9. Respond to stimuli

10. Reproduction

11. Growth and development

12. Homeostasis

13. Adaptability and change over time

Order the following units of matter from simplest to most complex.

Organelle	Atom	Cell	Organism	Molecule	Organ	System	Tissue

14. Atom

15. Molecule

16. Organelle

17. Cell

18. Tissue

19. Organ

20. System

21. Organism

Answer the following question.

22. A diagram of the relationships of the ancestry of all organisms is called a __Phylogenetic Tree or Diagram__

Circle the best answer.

23. Which complex molecule do all living organisms have in common?
    a. Chlorophyll
    b. Cellulose
    c. Sodium chloride
    d. DNA

24. How organisms interact with each other throughout the living world is the definition of
    a. Evolution
    b. Interdependence
    c. Natural selection
    d. Diversity

25. The concept of natural selection is based on the idea that certain favorable traits will more likely lead to successful survival and ____ of a species.
    a. Growth and development
    b. Reproduction
    c. Homeostasis
    d. Ability to respond to stimuli

26. The branch of biology that studies organisms interacting with each other and the environment is called
    a. Zoology
    b. Epidemiology
    c. Ecology
    d. Agronomy

27. The process by which inherited characteristics of a population change over generations so that new and genetically distinct populations and species develop is called
    a. Evolution
    b. Natural selection
    c. Interdependence
    d. Unity

28. Plants and animals are part of the domain ____.
    a. Bacteria
    b. Eukarya
    c. Prokarya
    d. Archaea

Choose an ecosystem and describe the interdependence within that ecosystem using specific examples of plants, animals, and energy sources.

29. Any description of an aquatic or terrestrial ecosystem where a chain of feeding relationships exists and a simple description of how each organism has an effect on the others.

30. Label the primary parts of this microscope.

a. Objectives

b. Stage

c. Light source

d. Ocular

e. Arm

f. Coarse focus knob

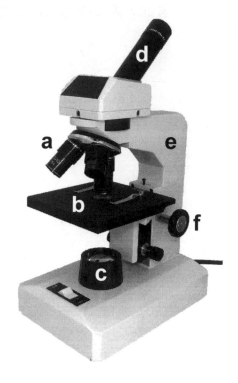

CHAPTER 3 TEST: Biochemistry

Name:_____ Date:_____ Score:_____

Circle the best answer.

1. What are the products in the hydrolysis of ATP?
   a. ATP and water
   b. ADP, phosphate, and energy
   c. ADP, water, and phosphate
   d. Ribose, adenine, and phosphate

2. How many covalent bonds is a carbon atom able to form with other compounds or elements?
   a. 1
   b. 2
   c. 3
   d. 4

3. Which structures are typically not formed by carbon molecules?
   a. Ring
   b. Inorganic
   c. Straight chain
   d. Branched chain

4. Saturated fats are typically
   a. Polar
   b. Liquid at room temperature
   c. Solid at room temperature
   d. Composed of carbon rings filled with hydrogen

5. Organic molecules that catalyze reactions in living systems are
   a. Phospholipids
   b. Enzymes
   c. Polysaccharides
   d. Steroids

6. What is a compound found in all cells that supplies the energy for cellular functions?
   a. Phosphate
   b. RNA
   c. ATP
   d. DNA

7. Enzymes catalyze reactions by
   a. Becoming chemically changed and reacting with the substrate
   b. Permanently linking to the substrate, creating a larger molecule
   c. Changing the temperature and pH of the substrate
   d. Linking to the substrate and weakening bonds within the substrate

8. The compound that is stored as glycogen in animals and starch in plants is
   a. Alcohol
   b. Cellulose
   c. Glucose
   d. Fructose

9. Molecules with the same molecular formula but different structures are called
   a. Phospholipids
   b. Isomers
   c. Nonorganic
   d. Steroids

10. In a triple bond, ____ pair(s) of electrons are shared between two C atoms.
    a. One
    b. Two
    c. Three
    d. Four

11. Amino acids become linked together by peptide bonds during ____ reactions.
    a. Condensation
    b. Redox
    c. Hydrolysis
    d. Oxidation

12. The breakdown of a polymer involves ____.
    a. Hydrolysis
    b. Dissociation
    c. Oxidation
    d. Condensation

13. ATP contains ____ phosphate groups.
    a. One
    b. Two
    c. Three
    d. Four

14. The most important function of a nucleic acid is ____.
    a. Catalyzing chemical reactions
    b. Forming a barrier between the inside and the outside of the cell
    c. Storing energy
    d. Storing information related to heredity and cell function

15. The different shapes and functions of different proteins are determined by ____.
    a. The R groups of the amino acids they are bonded to
    b. The amino groups of the amino acids they are bonded to
    c. The carboxyl groups of the amino acids they are bonded to
    d. Whether or not they contain amino acids

16. How many different types of monomers are found in proteins?
    a. 100
    b. 20
    c. 5
    d. 1

17. Glucose, fructose, and galactose are
    a. Monosaccharides
    b. Disaccharides
    c. Polysaccharides
    d. Lipids

Write the correct letter in the blank before each numbered item.

____E____ 18. Nucleotide

____H____ 19. Hydrolysis

____F____ 20. Steroid

____G____ 21. Amino acid

____A____ 22. Condensation reaction

____C____ 23. Glucose

____D____ 24. Fatty acid

____B____ 25. Functional group

A. Forms large molecules from smaller ones

B. Influences the characteristics of molecules

C. Monomer of polysaccharides

D. Monomer of lipids

E. Component of nucleic acids

F. Lipid not composed of fatty acids

G. Monomer of proteins

H. Breaks large molecules into smaller ones

The formation of sucrose from glucose and fructose is represented by the chemical reaction shown below. Answer the following questions relative to the diagram.

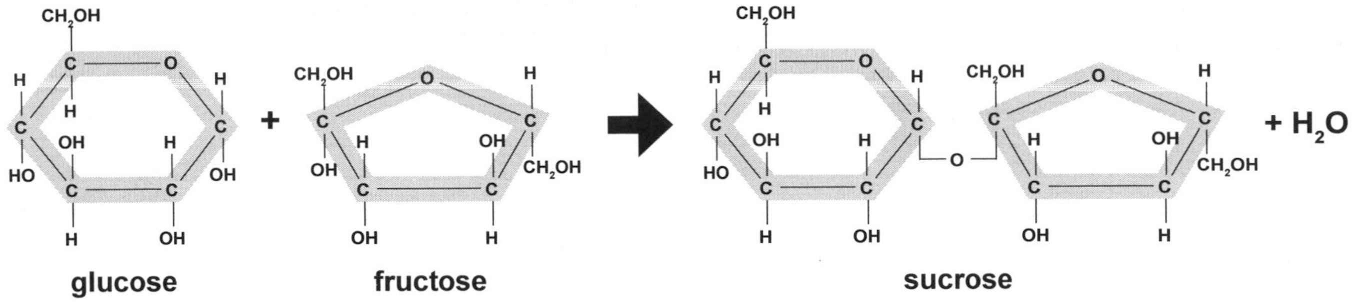

26. What are the reactants of the forward (left to right) reaction? Glucose and fructose
27. What are the products of the forward (left to right) reaction? Sucrose and water
28. What type of reaction is this? (left to right) Condensation
29. What are the reactants of the reverse reaction? (right to left) Sucrose and water
30. What type of reaction is this? (right to left) Hydrolysis

In the diagram of the molecules below, draw in lines as necessary to indicate the presence of any C=C double bonds.

31.

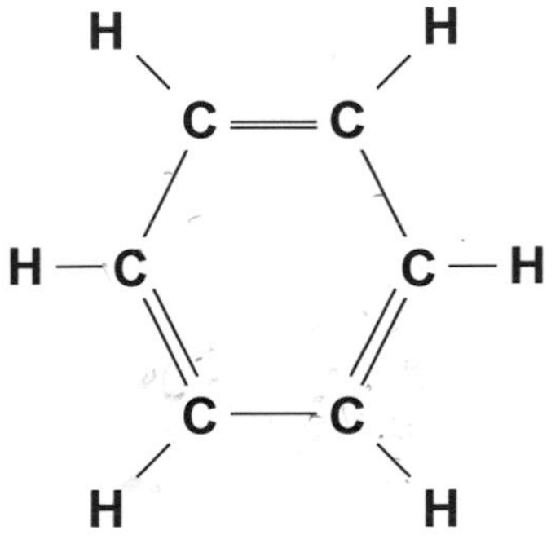

32.

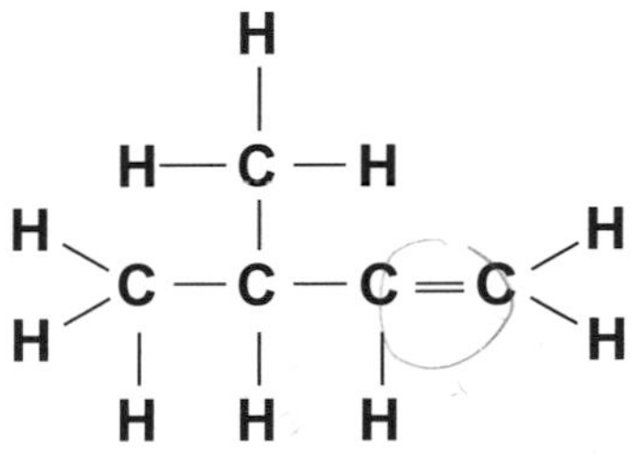

33.

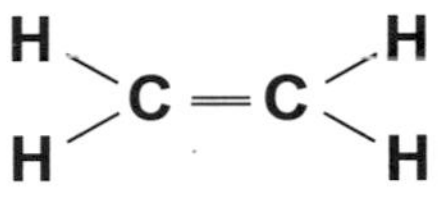

The following diagrams illustrate a variety of chemical structures. Write the correct name from the following list in the blank below each diagram. Not every word will be used.

Polypeptide Fatty Acid	Nucleotide Protein	Amino Acid ATP	Disaccharide Polysaccharide	Phospholipid Monosaccharide	Triglyceride Nucleic Acid

34. Triglyceride

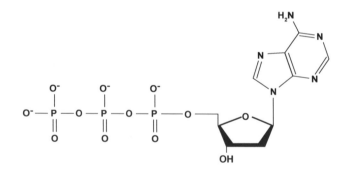

35. Amino Acid

36. ATP

37. Nucleotide

38. Disaccharide

39. Nucleic Acid (DNA)

40. Polypeptide

41. Explain the difference between type 1 and type 2 diabetes and their respective causes. (4 pts.)

Type 1 diabetes is typically a juvenile onset where a child's pancreas produces ineffective insulin or insufficient insulin. It is usually genetic. Type 2 diabetes is usually adult onset and caused by poor diet and exercise habits that cause the cells of the pancreas to decrease insulin production.

42. Describe the function and structure of DNA, its monomers, and the bonds that hold it together. (5 pts.)

DNA is a double helix structure made up of two complementary strands. Each strand is made up of repeating subunits called nucleotides. Each nucleotide is made up of a sugar, deoxyribose, a phosphate group, and one of four different nitrogen bases. Each nucleotide is held together by covalent bonds, and the two strands are held together by hydrogen bonds. The sugar and phosphate form the uprights of the double helix, while the nitrogen bases form the rungs. The function of DNA is to store and pass on the genetic code to new cells and to direct cell activities.

CHAPTER 4 TEST: Cell Structure and Function

Name:_____ Date: _____ Score: _____

Circle the best answer.

1. Which is not true of the central vacuole?
   a. It is a large, fluid-filled vacuole.
   b. It can consume up to 90% of a cell's volume.
   c. It forms from smaller vacuoles fusing together.
   d. Its primary function is to store glycogen as starch.

2. As a cell becomes smaller, its surface area ____ relative to its volume.
   a. Increases
   b. Decreases
   c. Stays the same
   d. Becomes less important

3. Which of the following is not part of the cell theory?
   a. All living things are made of one or more cells.
   b. All cells contain the same organelles.
   c. Cells are the basic units of structure and function in organisms.
   d. All cells arise from existing cells.

4. A cell's shape, size, and organization are determined by
   a. Its environment
   b. Its function
   c. Its temperature and pH
   d. The quantity of phospholipids in its membrane

5. Which of the following would you not find in an animal cell?
   a. Phospholipids
   b. Endoplasmic reticulum
   c. Nucleoid
   d. Mitochondria

6. Which part of the plasma membrane helps cells recognize each other?
   a. Phospholipids
   b. Enzymes
   c. Glycoproteins
   d. Sterols

7. Viruses, bacteria, and old organelles within a cell are broken down by the
   a. Ribosomes
   b. Lysosomes
   c. Rough ER
   d. Smooth ER

8. Organelles that are surrounded by a lipid bilayer and contain DNA are the
   a. Nucleus, chloroplasts, and mitochondria
   b. Nucleus, endoplasmic reticulum, and ribosomes
   c. Nucleus, endoplasmic reticulum, and lysosomes
   d. Nucleus and Golgi body

9. Integral membrane proteins perform all of the listed activities except
   a. Transmitting signals across the cell membrane
   b. Identifying the cell type to surrounding cells
   c. Functioning as enzymes assisting chemical reactions inside the cell
   d. Helping move substances across the cell membrane

10. The nucleus of a cell contains all of the following except
    a. Chromosomes
    b. Mitochondria
    c. DNA
    d. RNA

11. The end products of photosynthesis include
    a. Carbon dioxide
    b. Oxygen and carbohydrates
    c. Proteins and water
    d. Carbon dioxide and sugars

12. What type of molecule can be found in/on the plasma membrane?
    a. Carbohydrate
    b. Protein
    c. Phospholipid
    d. All of the above

13. The lipid bilayer of the plasma membrane
    a. Provides a boundary between the cell and its surroundings
    b. Contains sterols
    c. Transports substances into and out of the cell
    d. All of the above

14. The organelles most numerous in the kidneys and liver that neutralize free radicals are
    a. Lysosomes
    b. Chromosomes
    c. Peroxisomes
    d. Glyoxysomes

15. The organelle responsible for modifying and packaging molecules for export is the
    a. Endoplasmic reticulum
    b. Golgi apparatus
    c. Ribosome
    d. Mitochondria

16. The cytoskeleton is made up of
    a. Microtubules
    b. Mitochondria
    c. Phospholipids
    d. All of the above

17. The scientist who described cells as "many little boxes" was
    a. Robert Hooke
    b. Anton van Leeuwenhoek
    c. Theodor Schwann
    d. Rudolf Virchow

18. The purpose of sterols in the plasma membrane is to
    a. Transport compounds across the membrane
    b. Act as a hydrophobic barrier to substances trying to pass through
    c. Act as glycoprotein cell markers
    d. Insulate the cell and give it structure

19. Chromoplasts
    a. Contain a variety of pigments except chlorophyll
    b. May be specialized for storing starch or different plant-specific compounds
    c. Are found only in green photosynthetic plants
    d. Work with lysosomes to break down microbes invading the plant cell

20. The smooth endoplasmic reticulum
    a. Is very abundant in cells producing large amounts of protein
    b. Builds lipids such as cholesterol and functions in detoxification in liver cells
    c. Serves as a site for ribosomal attachment
    d. Consists of one small and one large subunit assembled in the nucleolus

21. Lysosomes
    a. Usually contain digestive enzymes
    b. Destroy old or broken down cells and organelles
    c. Break down bacteria that get into a cell
    d. More than one of the above

22. The primary function of mitochondria is to
    a. Modify and package proteins for export
    b. Produce energy for cell activity
    c. Control most of the functions of a eukaryotic cell
    d. More than one of the above

True or False: Please clearly mark T for true or F for false on the blank line.

___T___ 23. Mitochondria contain their own DNA for organelle replication.

___F___ 24. DNA is found in the nucleus in the form of chromatin during cell division.

___T___ 25. The diameter of most cells is between 10 and 50 microns.

___T___ 26. Some cells use cilia and/or flagella for locomotion.

___F___ 27. Glucose is stored as cellulose in animal cells.

___T___ 28. Ribosomes are partially assembled in the nucleolus.

___F___ 29. Hydrophilic phospholipid heads make up the interior of the cell membrane.

Fill in the Blanks

30. A cell's __function__ influences its shape, size and internal organization.

31. The statement "Cells only arise from other cells" is part of the __cell theory__.

32. Cilia and __flagella__ are structures that enable cell movement.

33. The two bundles of microtubules located in the centrosome that function in nuclear division are called __centrioles__.

34. Ribosomes are found on the __rough__ endoplasmic reticulum.

35. ATP is an acronym for __adenosine triphosphate__.

36. The model that best describes the plasma membrane is the __fluid mosaic__ model.

37. Explain the two functions of DNA in cells.

   Stores genetic information and directs cell activities

38. Why can small cells move substances in and out more readily than large cells?

   Smaller cells have a greater surface area-to-volume ratio and so have more surface to move substances into and out of the cell.

39. Why are mitochondria important to the functioning of muscle cells in eukaryotes?

   Muscle cells are very active cells and require a lot of energy (ATP) to function efficiently. Multiple mitochondria would produce the energy they need.

40. Describe the structure, elements, and function of the cytoskeleton.

   The cytoskeleton is made up of protein tubes and filaments that move substances throughout the cell, facilitate movement within the cell, and function in cell division.

Label the following diagrams.

41. What type of cell is illustrated below?_____Plant cell (eukaryotic)_____

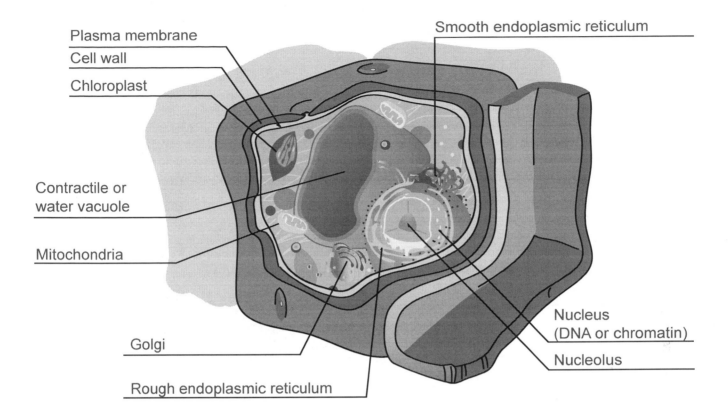

Plasma membrane
Cell wall
Chloroplast

Smooth endoplasmic reticulum

Contractile or water vacuole

Mitochondria

Golgi

Rough endoplasmic reticulum

Nucleus (DNA or chromatin)

Nucleolus

42. What type of cell is illustrated below?_____Animal cell (eukaryotic)_____

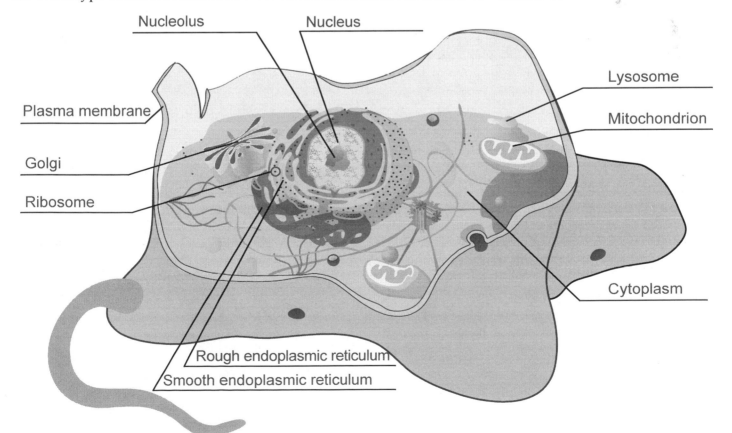

Nucleolus   Nucleus

Plasma membrane

Golgi

Ribosome

Lysosome

Mitochondrion

Cytoplasm

Rough endoplasmic reticulum

Smooth endoplasmic reticulum

CHAPTER 5 TEST: Homeostasis and Cell Transport

Name:_____ Date: _____ Score: _____

Write the correct letter in the blank before each numbered item.

___E___ 1. Kinetic energy

___I___ 2. Hypertonic solution

___H___ 3. Isotonic solution

___F___ 4. Facilitated diffusion

___A___ 5. Exocytosis

___B___ 6. Phospholipids

___C___ 7. Gated ion channel

___G___ 8. Hypotonic solutions

___D___ 9. Carrier protein

A. Moves waste out of a cell

B. Double layer of cell membrane

C. Usually controlled by electrical gradients

D. Shields molecule from lipid bilayer

E. Particle energy causing movement

F. Carrier proteins transporting molecules down a concentration gradient

G. May cause cytolysis

H. Causes cells to remain in equilibrium

I. May cause plasmolysis

Circle the best answer.

10. In the cell membrane, ion channels serve as

  a. Food molecules

  b. Cell markers

  c. Information receivers

  d. Passageways

11. The movement of water through a cell membrane is called

  a. Diffusion

  b. Active transport

  c. Osmosis

  d. Filtration

12. Which of the following is not a characteristic of active transport?

  a. It moves substances up a concentration gradient

  b. It requires energy from the cell

  c. It involves facilitated diffusion

  d. It relies on carrier proteins that often function as pumps

13. Facilitated diffusion is often used to transport

  a. People

  b. Molecules that are not soluble in lipids

  c. Water

  d. Sodium and potassium through a cell membrane pump

14. When particles move out of a cell through facilitated diffusion, the cell

  a. Gains energy

  b. Uses energy

  c. First gains and then loses energy

  d. Does not use energy

15. Molecules that are too large to be moved into a cell through the cell membrane can be transported across by

  a. Osmosis

  b. Endocytosis

  c. Exocytosis

  d. Simple diffusion

16. If the concentration of a sugar solution is lower outside the cell than inside the cell, which of the following will happen by osmosis?

    a. Sugar will move into the cell
    b. Water will move into the cell
    c. Sugar will move out of the cell
    d. Water will move out of the cell

17. Which of the following is an example of osmosis?

    a. The movement of ions from an area of high concentration to an area of low concentration
    b. The movement of ions from an area of low concentration to an area of high concentration
    c. The movement of water molecules from an area of high solute concentration to an area of low solute concentration
    d. The movement of water molecules from an area of low solute concentration to an area of high solute concentration

18. The excretion of materials to the outside of a cell by discharging them from vesicles is called

    a. Exocytosis
    b. Endocytosis
    c. Osmosis
    d. Facilitated diffusion

19. If the molecular concentration of a substance is the same throughout a space, the substance

    a. Has a large concentration gradient
    b. Is in equilibrium
    c. Will undergo diffusion
    d. Will undergo osmosis

20. All forms of active transport are dependent on

    a. ATP from the cell
    b. Ion channels
    c. Kinetic energy of the molecules
    d. Carrier proteins

21. Sodium-potassium pumps

    a. Move NA ions and K ions into cells
    b. Move NA ions and K ions out of cells
    c. Move NA ions into the cell and K ions out of the cell
    d. Move NA ions out of the cell and K ions into the cell

22. A structure that can move excess water out of a unicellular organism is a

    a. Carrier protein
    b. Ion channel
    c. Contractile vacuole
    d. Cell membrane pump

Write the correct letter in the blank before each numbered item.

____D____ 23. Crenation
____B____ 24. Vesicle
____H____ 25. Hypertonic
____G____ 26. Concentration gradient
____F____ 27. Hemolysis
____A____ 28. Hypotonic
____C____ 29. Phagocytosis
____E____ 30. Pinocytosis

A. Relatively low solute concentration
B. Membrane-bound organelle
C. Uptake of large particles
D. Shrinking of red blood cells
E. Uptake of solutes or fluids
F. Bursting of red blood cells
G. Concentration difference across a space
H. Relatively high solute concentration

Answer the following questions.

31. Name the three types of passive transport and two types of active transport. (2 pts.)

    Passive: Simple diffusion, osmosis, facilitated diffusion

    Active: Movement in vesicles, cell membrane pumps

32. What are the two fundamental differences between carrier proteins that participate in facilitated diffusion and carrier proteins that function as pumps? (2 pts.)

Facilitated diffusion requires no ATP and moves substances down their concentration gradient.

Cell membrane pumps move substances up their concentration gradient and require ATP.

33. Contrast endocytosis with exocytosis. Give a specific example showing the purpose of each process. (2 pts.)

Exocytosis releases substances outside the cell such as proteins made for export (insulin).

Endocytosis brings substances into a cell such as glucose or amino acids for making ATP or proteins.

34. Describe in detail the action of a sodium-potassium pump. (5 pts.)

The gradients of sodium and potassium must be maintained across a cell membrane,

so sodium is constantly being pumped out and potassium is being pumped in. This

establishes an electrical gradient and maintains membrane permeability. Three sodium

ions bind to the pump inside the cell. One molecule of ATP is cleaved, and the phosphate

binds to the pump. The sodium is released out of the cell while two potassium ions bind

to the pump outside and are then moved into the cell. The phosphate is released from the

pump and recycled.

Use the diagram below to answer questions 35-41.

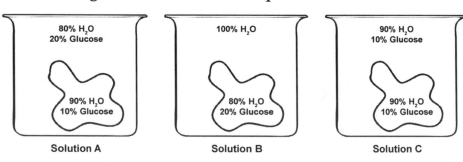

80% H₂O 20% Glucose	100% H₂O	90% H₂O 10% Glucose
90% H₂O 10% Glucose	80% H₂O 20% Glucose	90% H₂O 10% Glucose
Solution A	Solution B	Solution C

35. Solution A would be considered a/an _____hypertonic_____ solution relative to the solution inside the membrane.

36. Solution B would be considered a/an _____hypotonic_____ solution relative to the solution in the membrane.

37. Solution C would be considered a/an _____isotonic_____ solution relative to the solution inside the membrane?

38. By osmosis, will water move into or out of the sac in solution A?__Out__

39. By osmosis, will water move into or out of the sac in solution B? __Into__

40. By osmosis, will water move into or out of the sac in solution C? __Both__

41. If the cell in solution B was a red blood cell, it would likely undergo a process called _cytolysis_____.

CHAPTER 8 TEST: Cellular Reproduction

Name:_____ Date: _____ Score: _____

Circle the best answer.

1. DNA is copied during which phase of the cell cycle in eukaryotic cells?

   a. S phase

   b. Prophase

   c. G_2 phase

   d. Anaphase

2. The fibers that extend from the centrioles during mitosis are called

   a. Binary fibers

   b. Flagella

   c. Golgi fibers

   d. Spindle fibers

3. During the G_0 phase, cells

   a. Replicate their DNA

   b. Grow and mature

   c. Prepare for cell division

   d. Exit the cell cycle

4. During cell division, the DNA of a eukaryotic cell is tightly packed and coiled into structures called

   a. Histones

   b. Centromeres

   c. Chromatin

   d. Chromosomes

5. If an organism has a 2n number of 52, how many chromosomes will its gametes have?

   a. 104

   b. 9

   c. 26

   d. 18

6. Most prokaryotic cells reproduce by a process called

   a. Meiosis

   b. Mitosis

   c. Binary fission

   d. Spontaneous generation

7. The macromolecules that aid in the packing and coiling of DNA and help it to maintain its shape are called

   a. Glycoproteins

   b. Histamines

   c. Phospholipids

   d. Histones

8. Two similar copies of each autosome that carry the same traits and are the same size and shape are

   a. Hazardous

   b. Homologues

   c. Haploid

   d. Tetrads

9. During which phase of the cell cycle do tetrads form?

   a. Prophase of meiosis I

   b. Prophase of mitosis

   c. Prophase of meiosis II

   d. Interphase

10. The end result of mitosis is

   a. Four different haploid cells

   b. Two identical diploid cells

   c. Four identical diploid cells

   d. Two different diploid cells

11. Which organelle produces vesicles that form the cell plate?

a. Mitochondria

b. Endoplasmic reticulum

c. Golgi

d. Lysosomes

12. The purpose of synapsis and crossing-over in eukaryotic cells is to

a. Ensure genetic variability of offspring

b. Ensure even division of cell contents

c. Ensure that the spindle fibers attach to the correct tetrad during meiosis

d. Correctly align the chromatids in metaphase of mitosis

13. When crossing-over occurs

a. Chromatids are exchanged between cells

b. Corresponding genes are exchanged between homologues

c. DNA is exchanged in the form of chromatin

d. Tetrads link up with adjacent tetrads to exchange chromosomes

14. Haploid cells are formed for the first time during

a. Mitosis

b. Meiosis I

c. Meiosis II

d. Interphase

15. The process of oogenesis results in

a. Two identical egg cells

b. One oocyte and three oogonium

c. One oocyte and three polar bodies

d. Four different oocytes

16. The process of spermatogenesis results in

a. Two identical sperm cells

b. One spermatocyte and three spermatids

c. One spermatocyte and three polar bodies

d. Four different spermatocytes

17. The chromosomes of most prokaryotes are

a. A pair of DNA strands joined by a centromere

b. Haploid

c. A pair of homologous DNA molecules

d. A single circular strand of DNA

Answer the following questions.

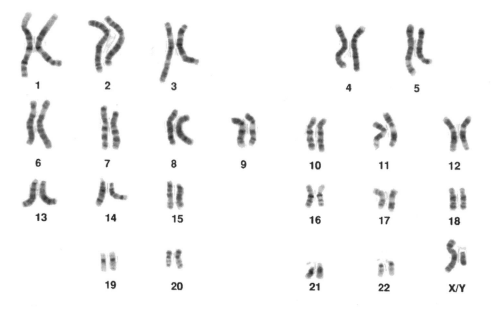

18. What is this picture called? _____ Karyotype

19. What is the sex of the person it represents? _____ Male

20. A human has how many *pairs* of autosomes in each cell? ___ 22

Use the circles below to draw and label the phases of mitosis in order.

 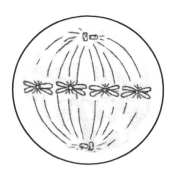  

21. Prophase 22. Metaphase 23. Anaphase 24. Telophase

Match the cell cycle phase on the right with the activities on the left. Choose the best answer.

D	25. DNA is copied and chromatids form
C	26. Chromatids separate at the centromere
A or F	27. Chromosomes line up on the equator
B or G	28. Nucleolar and nuclear envelopes break down
E or K	29. Spindle fibers disassemble
E or K	30. Chromosomes return to chromatin
G	31. Crossing-over occurs
F	32. Tetrads line up at the equator
H	33. Cytoplasm is divided between offspring
I	34. Homologues are pulled apart
D	35. Cells grow and mature
B or G	36. Centrioles and spindle fibers appear
E	37. Two new diploid nuclei are formed
J	38. Two new haploid nuclei are formed
J	39. Four new haploid nuclei are formed
D	40. Some cells exit the cell cycle

A. Metaphase
B. Prophase
C. Anaphase
D. Interphase
E. Telophase of mitosis
F. Metaphase of meiosis I
G. Prophase of meiosis I
H. Cytokinesis
I. Anaphase of meiosis I
J. Telophase of meiosis I
K. Telophase of meiosis II

Answer the following questions.

41. Describe the main differences in cytokinesis between plant and animal cells. (2 pts.)

A plant cell has the added cell wall that must be filled in. The Golgi apparatus produces vesicles that fill in the missing sections of the cell wall called the cell plate.

42. Explain why crossing-over is important.

Gene exchange between homologues ensures an endless genetic variety of gametes so that when two gametes join to form a new organism, no two are ever alike.

43. Describe the structure of a chromosome. (4 pts.)

DNA is replicated so that each cell has two identical copies. The strands of DNA are tightly coiled and wound around proteins called histones. The DNA is packed into two identical sister chromatids. The sister chromatids are held together by a centromere. This is a chromosome made up of two identical chromatids.

44. Compare the processes of spermatogenesis with that of oogenesis. (2 pts.)

Spermatogenesis results in four different viable spermatocytes from each diploid germ cell. Oogenesis results in one viable egg and three polar bodies from each diploid germ cell.

Label the diagram.

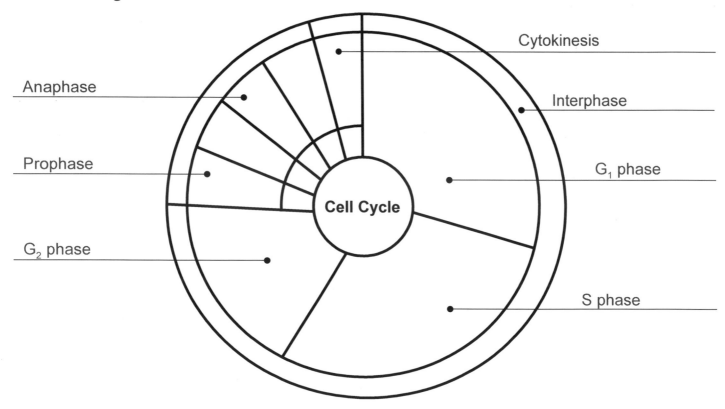

Cytokinesis

Anaphase

Interphase

Prophase

G_1 phase

G_2 phase

Cell Cycle

S phase

Label the phases of each cell cycle below.

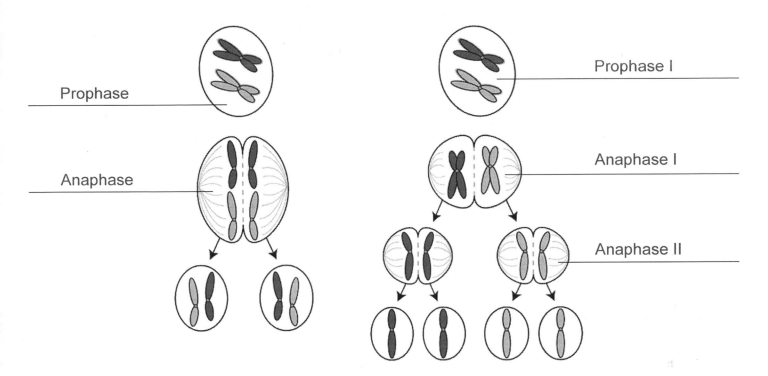

Prophase

Anaphase

Prophase I

Anaphase I

Anaphase II

CHAPTER 10 TEST: DNA, RNA, and Protein Synthesis

Name:_____ Date: _____ Score: _____

Circle the best answer.

1. The first scientists to propose that DNA was a double-stranded helix were
    a. Cambridge and King
    b. Franklin and Wilkins
    c. Watson and Crick
    d. Hershey and Chase

2. Which is **not** true of DNA?
    a. It is made up of nucleotides.
    b. The two strands are held together by peptide bonds.
    c. Sugar and phosphate groups are identical in all nucleotides.
    d. Each full turn of a helix holds ten nucleotide pairs.

3. The double-ring nitrogenous bases include or are called
    a. Pyrimidines
    b. Thymine
    c. Purines
    d. Cytosine

4. Bases complementary to adenine and guanine in DNA are respectively
    a. Thymine and cytosine
    b. Cytosine and adenine
    c. Uracil and cytosine
    d. Guanine and adenine

5. Base-pairing rules dictate that a strand of DNA with the base sequence of ATCGTCAATC will form an opposite base sequence of
    a. GCATCAGGCA
    b. TACGAGTTTG
    c. TAGCAGTTAG
    d. UAGCAGUUAG

6. Nitrogenous bases form ____ bonds with each other to hold complementary DNA strands together.
    a. Covalent
    b. Hydrogen
    c. Peptide
    d. Ionic

7. If the percentage of thymine on a DNA strand is 40%, what will the percentage of guanine be?
    a. 40%
    b. 10%
    c. 60%
    d. 50%

8. The main purpose of DNA replication in cells is
    a. To copy genetic information for cell division
    b. To form a template for protein synthesis
    c. To serve as storage for unused nucleotides
    d. To serve as a template for carbohydrate production

9. In DNA replication, the enzyme ____ works to separate the H bonds and the strands.
    a. DNA polymerase
    b. Helicase
    c. DNA ligase
    d. Promoters

10. In DNA replication, complementary bases are added by the enzyme ____.
    a. DNA polymerase
    b. Helicase
    c. DNA ligase
    d. RNA polymerase

11. As DNA separates for replication, the Y-shaped region that results is called a
    a. Promoter
    b. Start codon
    c. Dimer
    d. Replication fork

12. The end result of DNA replication without mutation is
    a. Two identical and separate DNA molecules
    b. Two similar and separate DNA molecules
    c. A single similar strand of RNA
    d. A single identical strand of RNA

13. The enzyme that later joins the gaps in the newly copied strand of DNA is
    a. DNA polymerase
    b. Helicase
    c. DNA ligase
    d. Photolyase

14. DNA replication in prokaryotes takes place in/on the
    a. Cytoplasm
    b. Nucleus
    c. Mitochondria
    d. Ribosome

15. Newly synthesized DNA base pairs in most organisms are proofed and repaired by the enzyme
    a. DNA polymerase
    b. Helicase
    c. DNA ligase
    d. Photolyase

16. Thymine dimers are two thymine bases linked together by a _____ bond
    a. Covalent
    b. Hydrogen
    c. Peptide
    d. Ionic

17. A segment of DNA that is located on a chromosome and codes for a hereditary characteristic is a
    a. DNA molecule
    b. Chromatid
    c. Gene
    d. Nucleic acid

18. The construction of an RNA template from DNA is called
    a. Replication
    b. Transcription
    c. Translation
    d. Excision

19. RNA is
    a. A nucleic acid made up of ribose, phosphate, and nitrogenous bases
    b. A protein made up of ribose, phosphate, and nitrogenous bases
    c. A DNA template made up of ribose, nitrogen, and adenine
    d. A five-ring sugar with nitrogen and adenine

20. Which of the following molecules bonds to a specific amino acid?
    a. mRNA
    b. rRNA
    c. tRNA
    d. DNA

21. Which is not one of the three major types of RNA?
    a. Ribosomal
    b. Transfer
    c. Carrier
    d. Messenger

22. The specific nucleotide sequence on the DNA where transcription is initiated is called the
    a. Replication fork
    b. Promoter
    c. RNA polymerase
    d. Start codon

23. A specific sequence of nucleotides that marks the end of a gene is called a/an

a. Stop codon

b. Termination signal

c. RNA polymerase

d. End code

24. In eukaryotic cells, DNA replication takes place

a. At the beginning and end of a DNA strand

b. In two directions around a circular chromosome

c. At many points on and in both directions of a DNA strand

d. At both ends of the DNA strand in both directions

25. If a DNA strand had the bases ATTACGCCA, its transcribed RNA strand would contain the bases

a. TAATGCGGT

b. TUUTGCGGT

c. UAAUGCGGU

d. TAATUCUUT

26. Amino acids are assembled based on instructions encoded in the sequence of nucleotides on the

a. mRNA

b. tRNA

c. rRNA

d. cRNA

27. A specific sequence of three nucleic acids on an mRNA that code for an amino acid are called a

a. Peptide

b. Promoter

c. Codon

d. Anticodon

28. The start codon AUG that always codes for the beginning of transcription is the code for

a. Alanine

b. Phenylalanine

c. Methionine

d. Methylamine

29. Amino acids are joined to one another by which type of bond?

a. Covalent

b. Hydrogen

c. Peptide

d. Ionic

30. How many different amino acids must be present for protein synthesis?

a. 200

b. 25

c. 30

d. 20

31. Translation takes place in/on the

a. Nucleus

b. Ribosome

c. DNA strand

d. Mitochondria

32. An anticodon AUG would look for the codon ___ to bind to.

a. TAC

b. UAC

c. UTA

d. UTC

33. The newly made polypeptide falls off when the ribosome reaches the

a. Stop codon

b. Termination signal

c. RNA polymerase

d. End code

34. Which is not true with regard to translation?

a. Several ribosomes can be translating a strand of mRNA at one time.

b. In prokaryotes, translation and transcription can occur simultaneously.

c. In eukaryotes, translation takes place in the nucleus so transcription and translation can never occur simultaneously.

d. A new ribosome begins translating as soon as the preceding ribosome has moved aside.

Use the diagram of the structure of DNA below to answer questions 35-37.

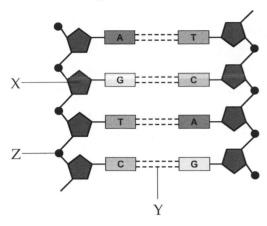

35. The structure labeled X represents

  a. Nitrogenous base

  b. Deoxyribose

  c. Amino acid

  d. Phosphate group

36. Which type of bond will form at the point labeled Y?

  a. Peptide

  b. Covalent

  c. Hydrogen

  d. Nitrogen

37. The structure labeled Z represents

  a. Nitrogenous base

  b. Phosphate

  c. Ribose

  d. Deoxyribose

Answer the following question.

38. Explain the differences between transcription and translation. (4 pts.)

Transcription occurs in the nucleus of a eukaryotic cell, and its purpose is to produce a template of mRNA from a gene. This template carries the genetic code for the production of a specific protein. Translation occurs in the cytoplasm on the ribosomes. Its purpose is to assemble a sequence of amino acids into a polypeptide based on the code of the mRNA.

Complete the following on the diagram below.

39. Transcribe the adjacent strand of DNA (Strand 2).

40. Transcribe the DNA.

41. Translate these same nucleotides to the mRNA strand where it docks on the ribosome.

42. Fill in the anticodons on the tRNA molecules according to the codons on the mRNA.

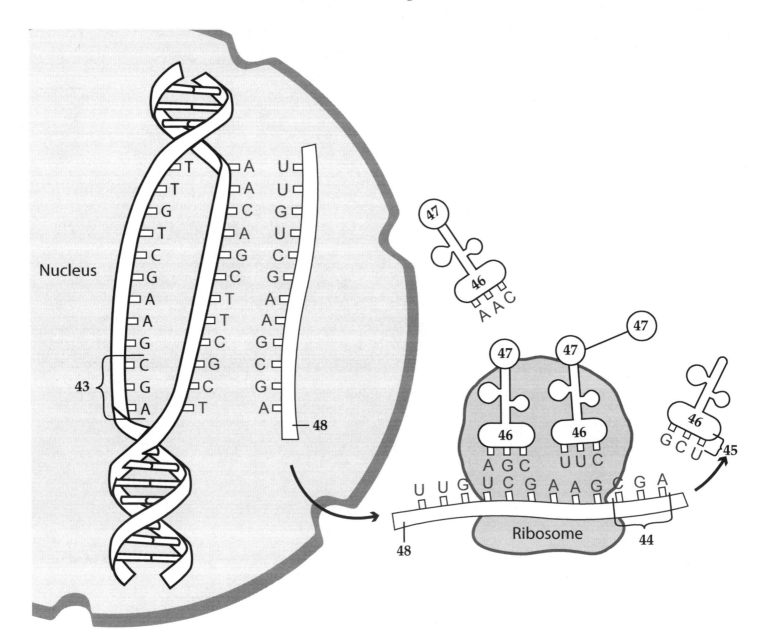

Label the diagram on the lines below.

43. Base triplet

44. Codon

45. Anticodon

46. tRNA

47. Amino acids

48. mRNA

CHAPTER 9 TEST: Fundamentals of Genetics

Name:_____ Date: _____ Score: _____

Choose the best answer. Assume complete dominance unless otherwise stated.

1. An organism that is heterozygous for fur color would have the genotype
   a. BB
   b. Bb
   c. bb
   d. BBbb

2. The P generation is also called
   a. The F1 generation
   b. The F2 generation
   c. The Px generation
   d. True-breeding

3. When an organism has inherited two of the same alleles of a gene from both parents, it is considered _____ for that trait.
   a. Hereditary
   b. Heterozygous
   c. Homozygous
   d. Crossing-over

4. A cross in which a single characteristic is tracked is called
   a. A self-pollinated cross
   b. A test cross
   c. A monohybrid cross
   d. A dihybrid cross

5. A homozygous individual could have any of the following genotypes except
   a. PPpp
   b. Pp
   c. PP
   d. pp

6. In a monohybrid cross between a homozygous dominant parent and a homozygous recessive parent, one would predict the genotype ratio of offspring to be
   a. 3:4
   b. 2:4
   c. 1:4
   d. 4:0

7. In a monohybrid cross between two heterozygous parents, one would expect the genotype ratio offspring to be
   a. 1pp:3PP
   b. 3PP:1pp
   c. 1PP:2Pp:1pp
   d. 1:0 Pp

8. In frogs, green skin is dominant. A green frog is crossed with a white albino frog. If the army of baby frogs contains a white offspring, the genotype of the green frog is probably _____.
   a. Homozygous dominant
   b. Heterozygous
   c. Homozygous recessive
   d. None of the above

9. To determine the genotype of an individual who exhibits the dominant phenotype, you would cross that individual with one who is
   a. Heterozygous dominant
   b. Heterozygous recessive
   c. Homozygous dominant
   d. Homozygous recessive

10. If two parents with dominant phenotypes produce an offspring with a recessive phenotype, then probably
    a. Both parents are heterozygous
    b. One parent is heterozygous
    c. Both parents are homozygous
    d. One parent is homozygous

11. A trait occurring in 300 offspring out of a total of 1,200 offspring has a probability of_____?
    a. 0.04
    b. 0.25
    c. 0.50
    d. 0.75

12. Suppose you have discovered a new species of butterfly. Some of the butterflies have blue spots and some have red spots. You cross a red spotted butterfly with a blue spotted butterfly, and all of the resulting offspring have purple spots. Which is the most likely genotype of the offspring?
    a. PP
    b. Pp
    c. pp
    d. rr

    BONUS: What is the most likely genotype of each parent? ___PP and pp___

13. Gregor Mendel, the father of genetics, was (circle all that apply)
    a. A monk
    b. A statistician
    c. A gardener
    d. Austrian

Answer the following questions.

14. Write the probability equation below.

    The number of times an event occurs
    _____

    The number of times the event could occur
    _____

15. A bushel of tomatoes shipped from the farm contains 130 yellow tomatoes and 390 red tomatoes that are randomly distributed among the bushel baskets based on the production of the two different plants. Assuming both types of plants produce equally, what is the percent probability of encountering a red tomato-producing plant over a yellow?

    130 + 390 = 520   390/520   75% Red

Write the correct letter in the blank before each numbered item.

___D___ 16. Genotype

___A___ 17. Monohybrid cross

___G___ 18. Heredity

___B___ 19. Allele

___C___ 20. Heterozygous

___E___ 21. Phenotype

___H___ 22. Gene

___F___ 23. Homozygous dominant

A. A cross involving one pair of contrasting traits

B. Each of two or more alternative forms of a gene

C. An organism having two different alleles for a trait

D. The genetic makeup of an organism

E. The description of the physical appearance of a trait

F. Having two similar dominant alleles for a trait

G. The transmission of characteristics from parent to offspring

H. A segment of DNA that controls a particular hereditary trait

Answer the following questions.

24. Describe Mendel's experiments on pea plants. Make sure you include all of the generations and the steps he took as he completed his experiments. Be thorough and include observations and conclusions. (8 pts.)

1. Mendel produced true-breeding plants for each trait of all seven characteristics by self-pollinating each one until he no longer reproduced any trait except the one he was breeding for. He produced fourteen true-breeding plants that he called his P generation.

2. He then cross-pollinated the two true-breeding traits for each characteristic—for example, a true-breeding white pea plant with a true-breeding purple pea plant. This resulted in offspring that only exhibited one of the colors; in this example, they were all purple. He concluded that one trait was dominant over the other. He called these his F_1 generation.

3. He then self-pollinated each of his F_1 generation plants, which resulted in a 3:1 ratio of traits, three purple and one white. He called these his F_2 generation. He concluded there were a pair of factors controlling the expression of the trait, one coming from each parent; in the presence of the dominant factor, the recessive factor would not be expressed.

25. Purple flowers are completely dominant in pea plants. How can you determine the genotype of a purple-flowering pea plant? Draw a Punnett square (s) to explain your answer. (3 pts.)

Perform a testcross (cross the dominant phenotype with a homozygous recessive phenotype) to determine the genotype of a dominant phenotype. If there are any offspring exhibiting the recessive trait, the unknown genotype would have to be heterozygous.   PP   Pp

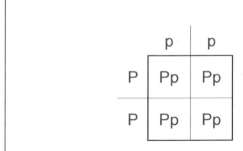

26. Explain the law of segregation and the law of independent assortment. (2 pts.)

The law of independent assortment says that traits sort independently of each other unless they are adjacent on a chromosome.

The law of segregation states that during meiosis, each newly formed gamete receives a full yet unique complement of both parents' genomes.

Fill in the remainder of the diagram to answer questions 27-30.

Parents' Genotypes: PpRr x Pprr

	PR	Pr	pR	pr
Pr	PPRr	PPrr	PpRr	Pprr
Pr	PPRr	PPrr	PpRr	Pprr
pr	PpRr	Pprr	ppRr	Pprr
pr	PpRr	X	ppRr	pprr

27. This diagram represents a Punnett square of
    a. Dominant vs. Recessive cross
    b. Homozygous vs. Heterozygous cross
    c. **Dihybrid cross**
    d. Monohybrid cross

28. The genotype of the cell labeled X is ____Pprr____.

29. The final ratio of phenotypes for Purple and Round to white and oval is ____6:1____.

30. List the possible genotypes which produce the dihybrid phenotypes:
    Purple Round = PPRR, PpRR, PpRr, PPRr = 6

    white oval = pprr = 1

31. In goldfish, orange color is dominant over red, and dorsal tails are dominant over fan tails. Predict the genotypic and phenotypic ratios of offspring produced by crossing one parent heterozygous for both traits and one parent homozygous recessive for both traits. Fill in the Punnett square to illustrate your predictions.

OoDd

	OD	Od	oD	od
od	OoDd	Oodd	ooDd	oodd
od	OoDd	Oodd	ooDd	oodd
od	OoDd	Oodd	ooDd	oodd
od	OoDd	Oodd	ooDd	oodd

oodd

Genotype Ratio: ____4:4:4:4____

Phenotype Ratio: ____4:4:4:4____

CHAPTER 23 TEST: Bacteria

Name:_____ Date: _____ Score: _____

Circle the best answer.

1. Which structure would you most likely find in a bacterial cell?
   a. Nucleus
   b. Cell membrane
   c. Mitochondrion
   d. Chloroplast

2. Which of the following is not a method of movement used by bacteria?
   a. Gliding through a layer of slime
   b. Flagella
   c. Corkscrewlike motion
   d. Forceful expulsion of a contractile vacuole

3. A poison that is released from a dead Gram-negative bacteria is
   a. A pathogen
   b. An exotoxin
   c. An endotoxin
   d. A broad spectrum toxin

4. Bacteria can become resistant to antibiotics by _____.
   a. Secreting antibiotics
   b. Assisting passage of antibiotics through the cell wall
   c. Acquiring an R-plasmid for resistance
   d. Growing only on petri dishes

5. Which prokaryote would you most likely find in hot acidic water?
   a. Chemoautotroph
   b. Halophile
   c. Cyanobacterium
   d. Thermoacidophile

6. Archaea and bacteria are placed in separate domains because _____.
   a. Ribosomal RNA sequences are different..
   b. Archaea have peptidoglycan in their cell walls.
   c. Proteins of bacteria are missing amino acids.
   d. Bacteria lack organelles.

7. Which of the following bacteria would you most likely find in the human intestine?
   a. Enteric
   b. Cyanobacterium
   c. Thermoacidophile
   d. Borelia burgdorferi

8. Photoautotrophic bacteria obtain energy
   a. From the sun
   b. By oxidizing inorganic compounds
   c. By feeding on live organisms
   d. By feeding on dead or decaying material

9. Which type(s) of bacteria will be destroyed by the presence of oxygen?
   a. Obligate anaerobes
   b. Obligate aerobes
   c. Obligate aerobes and facultative anaerobes
   d. More than one of the above

10. Many bacteria have pili that are used to
    a. Aid in the process of binary fission
    b. Propel the bacteria through its environment
    c. Enclose the genetic material of the bacteria
    d. Adhere to surfaces and join bacterial cells for conjugation

11. Which of the following bacteria are thought to be responsible for establishing the Earth's oxygen-rich atmosphere?
    a. Methanogens
    b. Rhizobium
    c. Cyanobacteria
    d. Spirochetes

12. The bacteria responsible for the production of stomach ulcers is
    a. Rickettsia
    b. Nitrosomonas
    c. Escherichia coli
    d. Helicobacter pylori

13. A bacteria that is nitrogen fixing
    a. Converts oxygen into carbon and nitrogen
    b. Converts carbon into nitrogen and ammonia
    c. Converts atmospheric nitrogen into nitrate
    d. Forms nitrates from oxygen and ammonia

14. A Gram-positive bacteria stains ___ because it has a ___ amount of peptidoglycan in its cell wall.
    a. Purple, small
    b. Purple, large
    c. Pink, large
    d. Pink, small

15. Two examples of Gram-negative spirochetes are
    a. Treponema pallidum and Borelia burgdorferi
    b. Anabaena and Lactobacillus
    c. Clostridium botulinum and Agrobacterium
    d. E. coli and Clostridium tetani

16. The process that uses bacteria to break down pollutants is called
    a. Recombination
    b. Conjugation
    c. Bioremediation
    d. Fermentation

17. The antibiotic tetracycline attacks bacteria by
    a. Blocking protein synthesis
    b. Blocking the cell's ability to synthesize new cell wall materials
    c. Phagocytosis
    d. Ribosomal detrition

18. The first scientist to discover that heat kills most bacteria and institute sterilization technique was
    a. Louis Pasteur
    b. Paul Ehrlich
    c. Alexander Fleming
    d. Robert Koch

19. In 1928, this scientist discovered the antibiotic properties of penicillin.
    a. Louis Pasteur
    b. Paul Ehrlich
    c. Alexander Fleming
    d. Robert Koch

20. The thick structure around the outside of some bacteria that helps to protect the bacteria from harsh environmental changes is the _____.
    a. Cell membrane
    b. Glycocalyx
    c. Plasmid
    d. Capsule

21. The small circular replicating loops of DNA that carry the genes to help make bacteria antibiotic resistant are called
    a. Introns
    b. Plasmids
    c. Pili
    d. Glycocalyx

22. Prokaryotes that thrive and grow best in moderate temperatures are called
    a. Thermophiles
    b. Psychrophiles
    c. Mesophiles
    d. Halophiles

23. The pH at which most bacteria thrive and grow is
    a. 2.5-5.0
    b. 5.0-6.5
    c. 6.5-7.5
    d. 7.5-9.0

24. Most foodborne illness is transmitted by
    a. Inadequate or improper handwashing
    b. Salmonella-contaminated vegetables
    c. Unrefrigerated cooked food
    d. Undercooked or raw meat

Answer the following questions.

25. Where does photosynthesis take place in photoautotrophic bacteria? (Be specific.)

    Thylakoids embedded in the plasma membrane

26. What is a glycocalyx, and what function does it serve?

    A sticky sugar coat on the outside of the capsule of some bacteria that help the bacteria

    adhere to other bacteria and host tissues.

27. Name three environmental factors that affect the growth of bacteria.

    Oxygen levels, pH, and temperature

28. The evolution of populations of pathogenic bacteria that antibiotics cannot kill is called __resistance__.

29. List the compounds used to Gram stain bacteria in the order they are used. (4 pts.)

    a. Crystal violet   c. Acetone or alcohol

    b. Iodine   d. Safranin

30. Explain why antibiotic resistance among bacteria is increasing. (2 pts.)

    Antibiotics are frequently overprescribed or prescribed inappropriately, which allows

    bacteria to acquire DNA that makes them resistant. Also, patients frequently do not finish a

    prescribed course of antibiotics, allowing some microbes to survive to acquire DNA that lets

    them become antibiotic resistant.

Draw and label the three primary bacterial shapes below.

31. Bacillus	32. Coccus	33. Spirillum

True or False

   F   **34.** Conjugation is the most common type of reproduction in prokaryotes.

   T   **35.** The primary nutritional needs of prokaryotes are carbon and energy.

   F   **36.** Strep and staph are two different forms of spirochetes.

   T   **37.** Cellular respiration takes place in the cell membrane of most bacteria.

   T   **38.** Several different antibiotics are made from the bacteria actinomycetes.

   T   **39.** Bacteria is used to genetically modify food to make it pest resistant.

Label the diagram and describe the function of the structures below.

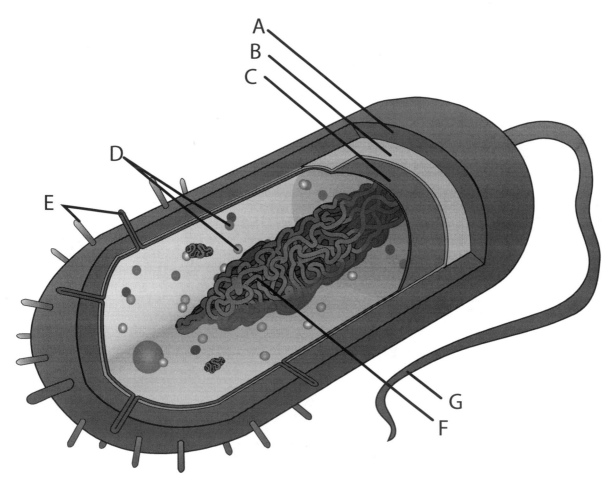

A.   Capsule protects the cell from host immune system and aids in pathogenesis.

B.   Cell wall gives the cell shape and structure as well as protection.

C.   Cell or plasma membrane controls what substances enter or exit the cell.

D.   Ribosomes provide a site for protein synthesis.

E.   Pilus aids in conjugation and helps bacteria to adhere to host tissues.

F.   DNA or nucleoid is the genetic information that controls cell activity.

G.   Flagella are used for locomotion.

CHAPTER 24 TEST: Viruses

Name:_____ Date: _____ Score: _____

Circle the best answer.

1. What are viruses made of?

    a. Enzymes and fats

    b. Carbohydrates and ATP

    c. Proteins and nucleic acids

    d. All of the above

2. The capsid of adenovirus is

    a. Helical

    b. Icosahedral

    c. Enveloped

    d. Spherical

3. How do viroids differ from viruses?

    a. Viroids do not contain a genome.

    b. Viroids are larger in size.

    c. Viroids only cause disease in plants.

    d. Viroids do not have a capsid.

4. Which of the following is a criterion for the classification of viruses?

    a. Whether they infect prokaryotic or eukaryotic cells

    b. Size

    c. The organelles they contain

    d. The presence or absence of an envelope

5. Which is an example of a common vector for human viral diseases?

    a. Birds

    b. Toilet seats

    c. Airplanes

    d. Bacteriophage

6. Which of the following is not effective in viral disease prevention or treatment?

    a. Antibiotics

    b. Vaccines

    c. Antiviral drugs

    d. Vector control

7. How do humans contribute to the increase in newly emerging viral diseases?

    a. Improper handwashing

    b. Mass vaccine programs for already eradicated diseases

    c. Inhabiting previously uninhabited lands and contracting new disease agents

    d. Drinking diet sodas

8. During which process does a phage kill its host?

    a. Lysogenic cycle

    b. Lytic cycle

    c. Transcription

    d. Cell replication

9. One viral disease that can occur in different forms at different ages of an infected person is

    a. Measles

    b. Smallpox

    c. Hepatitis

    d. Varicella

10. Phage DNA once integrated into a bacteria cell causes the bacteria to become a _____.

    a. Provirus

    b. Retrovirus

    c. Prophage

    d. Capsid

11. Viral Hepatitis A is most commonly spread by which means?

    a. Body fluids

    b. Fecal-oral

    c. Skin contact

    d. Air

12. HIV infects which cells?
    a. All white blood cells
    b. Neutrophils and monocytes
    c. Macrophage and T-lymphocytes
    d. Oncogenes and proto-oncogenes

13. Antiviral reverse transcriptase inhibitors
    a. Block transcription of viral DNA from RNA
    b. Help cells reduce viral load by quarantining the virus
    c. Block construction of new viral capsids
    d. Destroy the capsids of newly produced viruses

14. AIDS patients most frequently die from
    a. AIDS
    b. Pneumonias
    c. SARS
    d. Hemorrhagic fever

15. The first scientist to crystallize viruses and prove they were inanimate particles was
    a. Robert Koch
    b. Louis Pasteur
    c. Wendell Stanley
    d. Paul Ehrlich

Refer to virus A to answer questions 16-18. Refer to virus B to answer questions 19-21.

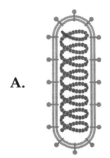

A.

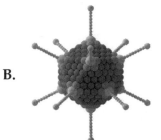

B.

16. The shape classification of virus A is
    a. Spherical
    b. Helical
    c. Bacteriophage
    d. Icosahedral

17. Its genome generally takes which form?
    a. Fragmented
    b. Linear or circular
    c. Pleated sheets
    d. Spiral

18. A common example of this virus is
    a. Rabies
    b. Chickenpox
    c. Influenza
    d. Polio

19. The shape classification of virus B is
    a. Spherical
    b. Helical
    c. Bacteriophage
    d. Icosahedral

20. Its genome generally takes which form?
    a. Fragmented
    b. Linear or circular
    c. Pleated sheets
    d. Spiral

21. A common example of this virus is
    a. Rabies
    b. Chickenpox
    c. Influenza
    d. Tobacco mosaic virus

22. Complete the following analogy:
    Person : Skin :: Virus : _____
    a. Genome
    b. Capsid
    c. Enzyme
    d. Viroid

Choose the best answer. Each answer is used only once.

___D___ 23. Protein coat

___F___ 24. Genome

___A___ 25. Phospholipid bilayer

___E___ 26. Oncogene

___G___ 27. Enzyme

___B___ 28. Lytic cycle

___H___ 29. Lysogenic cycle

___C___ 30. Proto-oncogene

A. Envelope

B. Virulent

C. Cell growth

D. Capsid

E. Cell replication

F. RNA or DNA

G. Reverse transcriptase

H. Temperate

Same rules. Match the virus to the symptoms or disease it may cause.

___B___ 31. Adenovirus

___D___ 32. Rhabdovirus

___F___ 33. HIV

___G___ 34. Varicella

___I___ 35. Poxvirus

___H___ 36. HPV

___E___ 37. Herpes virus

___A___ 38. Hepatitis virus

___C___ 39. Ebola virus

A. Liver cancer

B. Respiratory infection

C. Hemorrhagic fever

D. Rabies

E. Cold sores

F. AIDS

G. Shingles

H. Cervical cancer

I. Smallpox

Label the diagram.

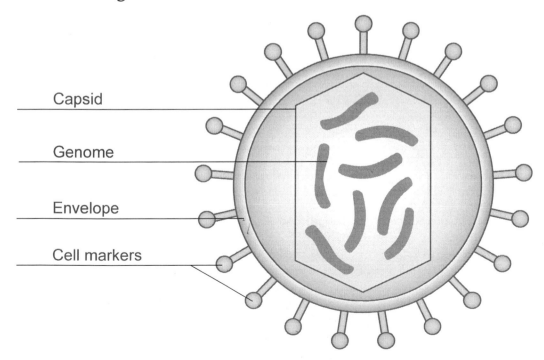

Capsid

Genome

Envelope

Cell markers

40. What virus could this be? ___Varicella or polio___

Answer the following questions.

41. AIDS is an acronym that stands for? ___Acquired immune deficiency syndrome___

42. How are viruses thought to have originated?

___Viruses likely originated from a naked piece of nucleic acid that entered a cell with a damaged___

___cell membrane. Evolution would have provided the capsid over time.___

CHAPTER 25 TEST: Protists

Name:_____ Date: _____ Score: _____

Circle the best answer.

1. Protists are classified in kingdom Protista
   a. Based on their means of motility
   b. Based on their means of food acquisition
   c. Based on their means of reproduction
   d. Based on the fact they are not clearly fungi, plant, or animal

2. Protists are thought to have evolved over time from a larger prokaryote engulfing a smaller one until they were unique and separate organisms. This characteristic is termed
   a. Parasitism
   b. Prosymbiosis
   c. Endosymbiosis
   d. Mutualistic

3. Protists are considered to be the most diverse kingdom in the biological world because
   a. They have many different body plans.
   b. They exhibit many different types of movement.
   c. They obtain food in many different ways.
   d. All of the above

4. Colonial unicellular organisms
   a. Can form a colony with areas of the colony minimally specialized to perform specific functions
   b. Can form multicellular organisms with job and cell specialization
   c. Can form into individual cells with specialized organelles for specific functions
   d. Live independently as single or multicellular organisms

5. Most protozoans are
   a. Autotrophic
   b. Heterotrophic
   c. Photosynthetic
   d. Pyrenoids

6. The internal flowing of an organism's cytoplasm is called
   a. Cytoplasmic feeding
   b. Pseudopodia extension
   c. Sarcodinian streaming
   d. Cytoplasmic streaming

7. The limestone formation on the floor of the ocean is thought to have developed from
   a. Dead protozoans
   b. Dead ciliates
   c. Dead sarcomastigophores
   d. Dead apicomplexans

8. The species radiolaria is classed in the subphylum
   a. Mycetozoa
   b. Sarcodina
   c. Sarcomastigophora
   d. Sporazoa

9. Which organism has more than one nuclei specialized for reproduction?
   a. Euglena
   b. Amoeba
   c. Paramecium
   d. Trypanosoma

10. Which phylum of protists has no means of locomotion in adult form?
   a. Apicomplexa
   b. Protozoa
   c. Sarcomastigophora
   d. Ciliaphora

11. The phylum of protists that has a specialized group of organelles used to more easily gain entrance to host cells and tissues is
    a. Apicomplexa
    b. Protozoa
    c. Sarcomastigophora
    d. Ciliaphora

12. Which phylum of protists kills more humans than any other group of pathogens?
    a. Apicomplexa
    b. Protozoa
    c. Sarcomastigophora
    d. Ciliaphora

13. An example of filamentous algae is
    a. Volvox
    b. Spirogyra
    c. Kelp
    d. Corallina

14. The structures in algae that help synthesize and store starch and also aid in photosynthesis are called
    a. Gametangia
    b. Pyrenoids
    c. Phytoplankton
    d. Phycobilin

15. Pigments that trap light in green algae are called
    a. Chlorophyll
    b. Rhodopsin
    c. Phycobilin
    d. Fucoxanthin

16. Phylum Phaeophyta contains the pigment _____, which gives it its brown color.
    a. Chlorophyll
    b. Carotenoids
    c. Phycobilin
    d. Fucoxanthin

17. Diatoms are unicellular protists from which phylum?
    a. Phaeophyta
    b. Chlorophyta
    c. Dinoflagellata
    d. Bacillariophyta

18. Which phylum of protists is responsible for producing red tide?
    a. Phaeophyta
    b. Rhodophyta
    c. Dinoflagellata
    d. Chrysophyta

19. Which phylum of protists stores energy as oil and may have played a role in the formation of early petroleum deposits?
    a. Phaeophyta
    b. Rhodophyta
    c. Dinoflagellata
    d. Chrysophyta

20. Protists from the phylum Myxomycota are also known as
    a. Water molds
    b. Cellular slime molds
    c. Plasmodial slime molds
    d. Pseudoplasmodial slime molds

21. A plasmodial slime mold will generally form a fruiting body when
    a. Its host dies
    b. The number of cells in the plasmodium becomes too large
    c. The environment becomes too cold
    d. Food and water become scarce

22. This phylum of protists has both spores and gametes with flagella.
    a. Oomycota
    b. Chytridiomycota
    c. Dictyostelida
    d. Myxomycota

True or False

_____T_____ **23.** Phytoplankton is the algae that forms the base of all marine food chains.

_____F_____ **24.** The clear elastic cell layer around some protists is called a pyrenoid.

_____T_____ **25.** Most sarcomastigophores are parasites.

Circle the best answer.

26. The plantlike protists are classified as protists and not plants because

  a. They are not photosynthetic.

  b. They have no cell wall.

  c. They have no roots, stems, or leaves.

  d. They lack the organelles of plants.

27. Paramecia reproduce sexually by

  a. Conjunction

  b. Conjecture

  c. Conjunctivation

  d. Conjugation

Write the correct letter in the blank before each numbered item.

_____C_____ **28.** Trypanosoma

_____D_____ **29.** Plasmodium

_____E_____ **30.** Toxoplasma gondii

_____B_____ **31.** Cryptosporidium

_____A_____ **32.** Sarcodina

  A. Entamoeba histolytica

  B. Flulike symptoms

  C. Sleeping sickness

  D. Malaria

  E. Toxoplasmosis

Answer the following questions.

33. Describe the process of feeding and digestion in a paramecium. (4 pts.)

The mouth pore is found in the funnel-like depression called the oral groove, which is lined with cilia for sweeping food into the mouth pore. Once inside the mouth pore, the food travels to the gullet, where food vacuoles are formed. Enzymes in the food vacuoles break down the food, and the nutrients are released into the cytoplasm. The anal pore moves undigested food particles out by contracting and expelling.

Use the following diagram for questions 34-35 and then label the diagram.

34. What phylum does this organism belong to? _Ciliaphora_

35. What is this organism? _Paramecium_

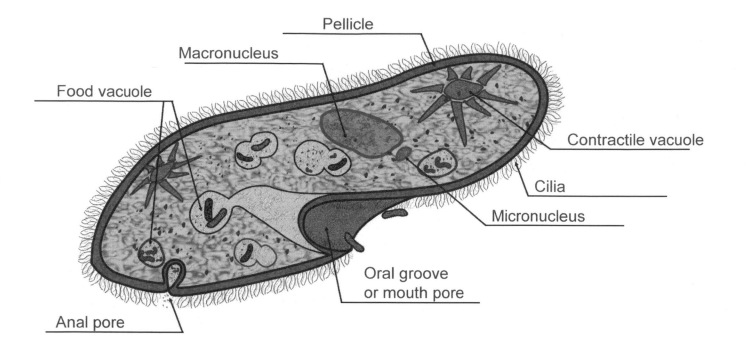

Use the following diagram for questions 36-38.

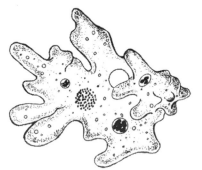

36. What type of organism is this?
Amoeba

37. Which phylum of animal-like protists would you place this organism in?
Protozoa

38. Which phylum of funguslike protists might you place this organism in?
Dictyostelida

Use the following diagram for questions 39-41.

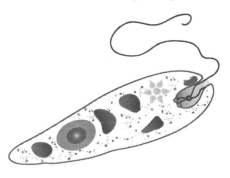

39. What organism is this?
Euglena

40. Which phylum of protists would you place this organism in?
Euglenophyta

41. Based on its characteristics, in which other phylum might you classify this organism?
Sarcomastigophora

CHAPTER 29 TEST: Plant Structure and Function

Name:_____ Date: _____ Score: _____

Circle the best answer.

1. The plant cell that makes up the bulk of the fleshy part of a fruit is ____.
   a. Parenchyma
   b. Florenchyma
   c. Sclerenchyma
   d. Collenchyma

2. The plant cell type dominant in plant tissues that are no longer growing is ____.
   a. Parenchyma
   b. Florenchyma
   c. Sclerenchyma
   d. Collenchyma

3. In a plant, the movement of sugar from its place of production to its place of storage is _____.
   a. Cohesion-tension
   b. Transpiration
   c. Evaporation
   d. Translocation

4. The opening and closing of stomata are regulated by the presence of which mineral?
   a. Sodium
   b. Potassium
   c. Magnesium
   d. Chlorine

5. The three basic organs of a plant are ____.
   a. Dermal, ground, and vascular
   b. Roots, stems, and leaves
   c. Parenchyma, collenchyma, and sclerenchyma
   d. Tracheids, vessel elements, and sieve tube members

6. Groups of cells working together to perform a certain function form a/an ____.
   a. Tissue
   b. Organ
   c. System
   d. Organism

7. The epidermis of a plant is made up primarily of ____.
   a. Irregularly shaped collenchyma cells
   b. Sclerenchyma cells that usually are dead at maturity
   c. Florenchyma cells that support herbaceous plants
   d. Parenchyma cells that may be living or dead

8. The small holes in the cuticle of a plant that function in gas exchange are ____.
   a. Pits
   b. Plates
   c. Stomata
   d. Cambium

9. Cacti would have a large number of which plant cell type?
   a. Parenchyma
   b. Florenchyma
   c. Sclerenchyma
   d. Collenchyma

10. Xylem and phloem are made up primarily of sclerenchyma cells arranged into
   a. Long systems of tubes
   b. Flattened systems of sacs
   c. Fibrous systems of threads
   d. Companion cells

11. Which plant would likely contain the least xylem?
    a. Evergreen tree
    b. Cactus
    c. Water lily
    d. Grass

12. The plant structure found on the end of a stem or root where cells continuously divide is
    a. Apical meristem
    b. Intercalary meristem
    c. Lateral meristem
    d. Bud scales

13. Secondary growth in plants occurs from which structure?
    a. Apical meristem
    b. Intercalary meristem
    c. Lateral meristem
    d. Bud scales

14. Specialized roots that grow from uncommon places are called
    a. Fibrous roots
    b. Taproots
    c. Root hairs
    d. Adventitious roots

15. Roots present in monocots where primary roots do not grow larger than the secondary roots are ____.
    a. Fibrous Roots
    b. Taproots
    c. Root Hairs
    d. Adventitious Roots

16. The xylem and phloem of a **leaf** are embedded in the
    a. Ground tissue
    b. Pith
    c. Dermal tissue
    d. Vascular cambium

17. One difference between monocot **stems** and dicot stems is that monocot stems usually
    a. Have vascular bundles arranged in a ring
    b. Replace primary tissues with secondary tissues
    c. Retain their primary growth pattern most of their lives
    d. Have significant secondary growth

18. In a **stem** cross section, an annual ring represents an abrupt change between
    a. Summerwood and springwood
    b. Heartwood and sapwood
    c. Bark and cork
    d. Xylem and phloem

19. The driving force for transpiration is provided by
    a. Water pressure in the roots
    b. Water tension in the stems
    c. Evaporation of water from the leaves
    d. The hydrolysis of ATP

20. Secondary xylem and phloem develop from which structure?
    a. Mesophyll
    b. Vascular cambium
    c. Petiole
    d. Epidermis

21. The common leaf type in which the blade is divided into leaflets is called
    a. Simple
    b. Compound
    c. Doubly compound
    d. Tendrils

22. The type of stem that grows on the surface of the soil and can produce a new plant is a
    a. Tuber
    b. Tendril
    c. Blade
    d. Stolon

23. Water movement from the plant roots up the stem relies on which two properties?

    a. Osmosis and diffusion
    b. Tension and attraction
    c. Cohesion and adhesion
    d. Transpiration and evaporation

24. The process by which a plant moves and then loses water is called _____.

    a. Transpiration
    b. Cohesion
    c. Adhesion
    d. Diffusion

25. Most photosynthesis occurs in a portion of the leaf called the _____.

    a. Vascular cambium
    b. Spongy mesophyll
    c. Palisade mesophyll
    d. Epidermis

26. Leaves that develop in full sun

    a. Are thicker
    b. Have more surface area per leaf
    c. Have larger chloroplasts
    d. Have minimal shading of one chloroplast over another

27. An adaptation that reduces water loss from leaves without diminishing photosynthesis is _____.

    a. Closing of the stomata at night
    b. Closing of the stomata during a water shortage
    c. The presence of a large number of stomata
    d. Epidermal hairs to limit transpiration

28. Modified cells on the epidermis that regulate gas and water exchange are called _____.

    a. Potassium pumps
    b. Guard cells
    c. Tracheids
    d. Mesophyll

29. The vascular cambium in dicot stems is located _____.

    a. Outside the phloem
    b. Between the xylem and phloem
    c. Just under the epidermis
    d. None of the above

30. Photosynthesis in leaves produces sugar for storage. The location of this storage is called the _____.

    a. Source
    b. Sink
    c. Sieve tube
    d. Vessel element

Correctly label the diagrams below.

31. What type of root is this?

    Taproot

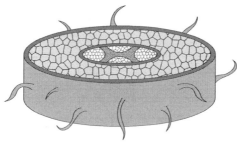

32. What is this plant organ?

    Root

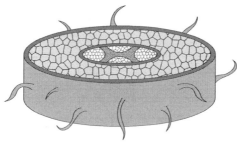

33. What is this plant organ?

    Leaf

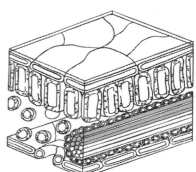

Correctly label the following diagram.

Terminal bud or apical meristem

Node

Internode

Lateral bud

Petiole

Taproot

Bonus: Lateral roots

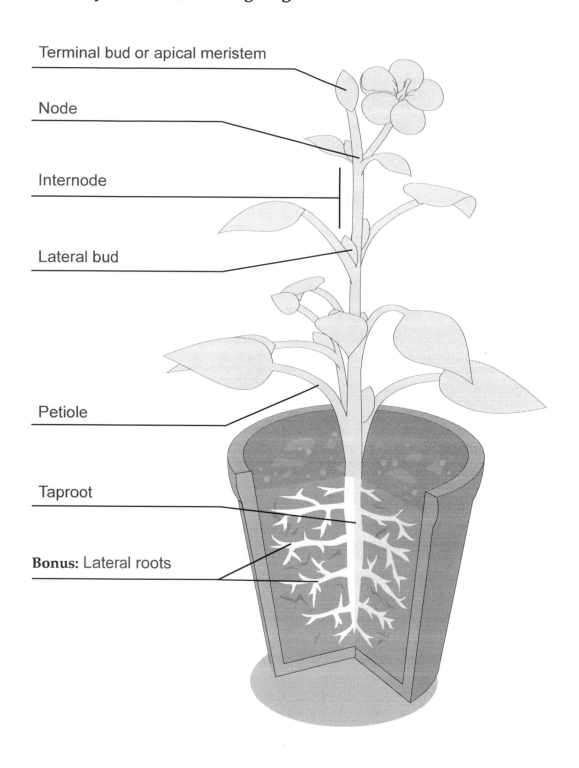

CHAPTER 32 TEST: Introduction to Animals

Name:_____ Date: _____ Score: _____

What are the four characteristics that all animals exhibit (at some point in their life cycle)?

1. Multicellular

2. Heterotrophic

3. Sexual reproduction

4. Movement or motility

Circle the best answer.

5. What is the cell process that leads to cell specialization in animals?
   a. Evolution
   b. Organization
   c. Division of labor
   d. Differentiation

6. What occurs immediately following fertilization?
   a. Meiosis
   b. Gastrulation
   c. Organogenesis
   d. Cleavage

7. Ectoderm : Skin :: Mesoderm : _____
   a. Nerves
   b. Stomach
   c. Lungs or gills
   d. Vertebrae

Answer the following question.

8. Animals are classified into phyla based on what primary characteristics? (4 pts.)
   Morphology, rRNA sequences, embryonic development, and fossil records

Circle the best answer.

9. Phylogenetic diagrams illustrate _____.
   a. The complexity of a group of organisms
   b. Which organisms have been classed into each phylum
   c. Evolutionary relationships between organisms
   d. Feeding and reproductive relationships between organisms

10. A fluid-filled cavity that forms following gastrulation is called a _____.
    a. Coelom
    b. Blastopore
    c. Blastocoel
    d. Archenteron

11. An animal that is able to produce both male and female gametes is called a/an _____.
    a. Polysexual
    b. Gastropod
    c. Indirect developer
    d. Hermaphrodite

12. Animals that undergo indirect development begin life as _____, while animals that undergo direct development begin as _____.
    a. Nymphs, larva
    b. Acoelomates, coelomates
    c. Larva, nymphs
    d. Zygotes, embryos

13. Which is not a part of an animal's morphology?
    a. Shape
    b. Coelom formation
    c. Symmetry
    d. Organization

14. Which does not belong in this list of vertebrates?
    a. Toads
    b. Birds
    c. Puppies
    d. Wasps

15. Which is not a function of the circulatory system?
    a. Carry nutrients to tissues
    b. Carry CO_2 to tissues
    c. Carry O_2 to tissues
    d. Carry waste to the excretory system

16. Organisms in which phylum are composed of only two embryonic germ layers?
    a. Porifera
    b. Mollusca
    c. Ctenophora
    d. Annelida

17. The deep cavity that becomes the gut during embryonic development is the _____.
    a. Coelom
    b. Archenteron
    c. Blastocoel
    d. Protostome

18. The three germ layers are organized from inside to outside in this order.
    a. Endoderm, ectoderm, mesoderm
    b. Ectoderm, mesoderm, endoderm
    c. Endoderm, mesoderm, ectoderm
    d. Ectoderm, endoderm, mesoderm

19. Tissues that arise from the endoderm are the _____.
    a. Skin, hair, and nails
    b. Muscles, bones, and circulatory
    c. Digestive, respiratory, and reproductive
    d. Nervous, endocrine, and integumentary

20. Animals that have no body cavity and have a solid interior are called _____.
    a. Coelomates
    b. Pseudocoelomates
    c. Acoelomates
    d. Noncoelomates

21. The fate of the blastopore in a deuterostome is to become the _____.
    a. Anus
    b. Gut
    c. Mouth
    d. Umbilicus

22. When the path or fate of a cell is fixed late in its development, the cleavage is said to be _____.
    a. Determinate
    b. Developed
    c. Ambiguous
    d. Indeterminate

23. The process of coelom formation in protostomes is called _____.
    a. Schizocoely
    b. Protocoely
    c. Enterocoely
    d. Blastocoely

24. Which statement best describes a gastrula?
    a. A hollow ball of cells
    b. A zygote
    c. A fetus
    d. A multilayered embryo

25. An animal exhibiting radial symmetry _____.
    a. Has a distinct top, bottom, front, and back
    b. Shows high degrees of cephalization
    c. Has a distinct top and bottom, but no front, back, right, or left
    d. Is usually a quadruped

26. Which phylum of invertebrates has no true tissues but cells specialized for specific functions?
    a. Porifera
    b. Cnidaria
    c. Mollusca
    d. Annelida

Match the phylum name on the left with the organism in that phylum on the right.

H	27. Porifera	**A.** Squid
G	28. Nematoda	**B.** Jellyfish
C	29. Platyhelminthes	**C.** Flatworm
E	30. Annelida	**D.** Sea star
B	31. Cnidaria	**E.** Segmented worm
D	32. Echinodermata	**F.** Crab
A	33. Mollusca	**G.** Roundworm
F	34. Arthropoda	**H.** Sponge

Answer the following questions.

35. What developmental feature indicates that echinoderms are more closely related to vertebrates than they are to other invertebrates?

They both undergo deuterostomal development.

36. What is the advantage of a multichambered heart, which is seen in all vertebrates?

A multichambered heart limits or eliminates the mixing of oxygenated blood with deoxygenated blood. It is much more efficient and seen in active animals with a high oxygen demand.

37. Describe the difference between an open and closed circulatory system. (2 pts.)

An open circulatory system utilizes a pump that sends blood or hemolymph into large vessels and then into the coelom so that gasses diffuse into and out of the coelomic fluid to be moved back into a vessel leading to the pump or heart. In a closed system, the blood remains in vessels so that gasses must diffuse across the vessels and into the tissues and back again. There is no mixing of oxygenated and deoxygenated blood. A closed system is more efficient for animals with high oxygen demand.

Label the organism based on the type of body cavities developed.

38. Pseudocoelomate   39. Coelomate   40. Acoelomate

Indicate the pattern of development illustrated by each diagram on lines 41 and 42. Label the indicated structures.

41. Protostomes   42. Deuterostomes

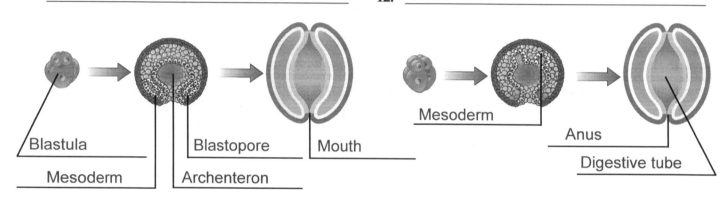

Blastula

Mesoderm

Blastopore

Archenteron

Mouth

Mesoderm

Anus

Digestive tube

Label the diagrams with the correct surface or directional term and answer the question below.

43. What type of symmetry do these animals exhibit?   Bilateral

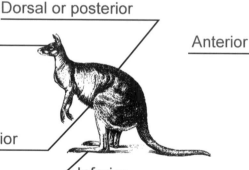

Dorsal or posterior

Superior

Ventral or anterior

Inferior

Anterior

Dorsal

Posterior

Ventral

Answer the following question.

44. Explain how identical twins develop. (2 pts.)

The blastula of an organism that is undergoing indeterminate cleavage becomes separated. Each half of the blastula develops into a complete organism. The two organisms will be identical since they have identical DNA.

CHAPTERS 33 & 34 TEST: Invertebrates I

Name:_____ Date: _____ Score: _____

Circle the best answer.

1. The common jellyfish moves from the blastula stage to a ciliated larva called a _____.
   a. Blastophore
   b. Colloblast
   c. Planula
   d. Gemmule

2. The genus Aurelia belongs to which class of cnidarians?
   a. Scyphozoa
   b. Anthozoa
   c. Cubozoa
   d. Hydrozoa

3. Which is not true of the general characteristics of Porifera?
   a. Hermaphroditic
   b. Multicellular
   c. True tissues and organs
   d. Sessile

4. Respiration in Porifera occurs through _____.
   a. Gills
   b. Lungs
   c. Simple diffusion
   d. Facilitated diffusion

5. The jellylike substance between the two cell layers that make up the body of a Porifera is _____.
   a. Mesoderm
   b. Mesohyl
   c. Mesoglea
   d. Mesophlegm

6. Pores in the body of the sponge wall where water enters the organism are the _____.
   a. Ostia
   b. Osculum
   c. Choanocytes
   d. Spicules

7. Spongin is _____.
   a. A tiny hard particle of calcium carbonate or silicon that makes the skeleton of a sponge
   b. A specialized cell for defense and catching prey
   c. Protein fibers that make up the skeleton of some sponges
   d. The jellylike substance between the two cell layers of a sponge

8. Bell-shaped cnidarians specialized for swimming occur in this form.
   a. Polyp
   b. Sessile
   c. Osculi
   d. Medusa

9. Cells that crawl around the body of a sponge and pick up and deliver nutrients are _____.
   a. Choanocytes
   b. Collar cells
   c. Colloblasts
   d. Amoebocytes

10. The inner cell layer of a cnidarian is the _____.
    a. Epidermis
    b. Endodermis
    c. Gastrodermis
    d. Mesodermis

11. The long coiled filament organelle specialized for paralyzing and capturing prey is _____.
    a. Nematocyst
    b. Colloblast
    c. Cnidocyte
    d. Apical organ

12. The characteristic that allows cells of a sponge to regroup into a new or same sponge is ___.

 a. Neogeneration
 b. Spontaneous generation
 c. Regeneration
 d. Recognition

13. This organ coordinates all of the body activities of a cnidarian.

 a. Contractile cells
 b. Apical organ
 c. Nerve net
 d. Cnidocytes

14. A freshwater hydra reproduces _____ during warm summer months.

 a. By gemmule formation
 b. Sexually
 c. Asexually
 d. Externally

15. Species Obelia and Physalia belong to which class of cnidarians?

 a. Anthozoa
 b. Hydrozoa
 c. Cubozoa
 d. Scyphozoa

16. The sea anemone and coral belong to which class of cnidarians?

 a. Anthozoa
 b. Hydrozoa
 c. Cubozoa
 d. Scyphozoa

17. The sensory structure found in most ctenophores that allows the animal to sense its position in the water as well as coordinate its movements is the _____.

 a. Nerve net
 b. Apical organ
 c. Colloblasts
 d. Gastrovascular cavity

18. The digestive system of cnidarians as well as their form of indirect development classify them as _____.

 a. Protostomes
 b. Deuterostomes
 c. Acoelomates
 d. Enterocoels

19. Flatworms have no need for circulatory or respiratory systems because _____.

 a. Their spherical body shape decreases surface area-to-volume ratios for osmosis
 b. The digestive system performs these functions
 c. The flattened body shape allows for diffusion of gasses into cells
 d. The coelom is bathed in blood and oxygen

20. Which of the following statements about tapeworms is not true?

 a. They can infect a person who eats undercooked beef.
 b. They belong to the genus Schistosoma.
 c. They can grow very large in human intestines.
 d. They do not have a digestive system.

21. Which of the following uses a snail as an intermediate host?

 a. Schistosoma
 b. Ascaris
 c. Planaria
 d. Obelia

22. The eggs of Ascaris _____.

 a. Are carried by human waste
 b. Can survive in the soil for years
 c. Develop into larvae in the intestine
 d. All of the above

23. A type of roundworm that lives a parasitic life is _____.

 a. Ascaris
 b. Enterobius
 c. Trichinella
 d. All of the above

24. The thick protective covering on endoparasitic flukes that prevents them from being digested by their hosts is the _____.
   a. Tegument
   b. Flame cells
   c. Cilia
   d. Mucous

25. Structures that help planarians deal with water entering their bodies by osmosis are _____.
   a. Flame cells
   b. Excretory tubules
   c. Cilia
   d. All of the above

26. Taenia saginatus is a tapeworm from the class _____.
   a. Turbellaria
   b. Trematoda
   c. Cestoda
   d. Nematoda

27. The knob-shaped organ with hooks and suckers on a tapeworm is called the _____.
   a. Proglottid
   b. Cuticle
   c. Mastax
   d. Scolex

28. The primary hosts of Taenia saginatus are _____.
   a. Cows
   b. Snails
   c. Pigs
   d. Humans

29. Nematodes are _____.
   a. Coelomates
   b. Acoelomates
   c. Pseudocoelomates
   d. None of the above

30. Cnidarians are _____.
   a. Coelomates
   b. Acoelomates
   c. Pseudocoelomates
   d. None of the above

31. Most trematodes enter their human host by _____.
   a. Contaminated food or water
   b. Contaminated meat
   c. Boring through the skin and into the blood vessels
   d. Eggs ingested on parasite-infected hands

32. Each mature tapeworm proglottid _____.
   a. Contains both male and female reproductive organs
   b. Contains fertilized eggs that develop into larvae
   c. Is eliminated in feces
   d. All of the above

33. The roundworm that feeds on blood from the intestinal wall of cats, dogs, and humans is the _____.
   a. Hookworm
   b. Enterobius
   c. Ascaris
   d. Filaria

34. The intestinal parasite causing trichinosis is _____.
   a. Taenia solium
   b. Ascaris
   c. Trichinella
   d. Filaria

35. The most common parasitic worm infection in the U.S. is _____.
   a. Ascaris
   b. Filaria
   c. Trichinella
   d. Enterobius

36. The parasitic nematode that uses a mosquito as its vector is the _____.
   a. Ascaris
   b. Filaria
   c. Trichinella
   d. Enterobius

37. The parasitic nematode affecting the lymphatic system and causing elephantiasis is _____.
    a. Ascaris
    b. Filaria
    c. Trichinella
    d. Enterobius

38. Which is not true of rotifers?
    a. They are 100-500 μm in size.
    b. They are free living and nonparasitic.
    c. They are multicellular with complex organ systems.
    d. They cannot survive outside water.

39. Which is not characteristic of a ctenophore?
    a. Colloblasts
    b. Apical organ
    c. Flagella
    d. Bioluminescence

Match the characteristic on the left to a phylum on the right.

E	40. Parthenogenesis	**A.** Platyhelminthes
B	41. Amoebocytes	**B.** Porifera
A	42. Acoelomates	**C.** Nematoda
A or E	43. Flame cells	**D.** Cnidaria
A	44. Proglottids	**E.** Rotifera
D	45. Cnidocytes	**F.** Ctenophora
A	46. Schistosoma	
D	47. Nerve net	
B	48. Choanocytes	
D	49. Medusa	
E	50. Mastax	

Answer the following question.

51. Describe two examples of symbiosis found among invertebrates and how each species benefits. (4 pts.)

    Clownfish live symbiotically with anemones. The anemones give the clownfish protection from predators, and the clownfish stir up food for the anemones.

    Some species of hydra live symbiotically with algae. The hydra provides a home and protection to the algae, and the algae produces energy and food for the hydra.

Correctly label the diagrams.

52. Which phylum does this organism belong to? _Porifera_

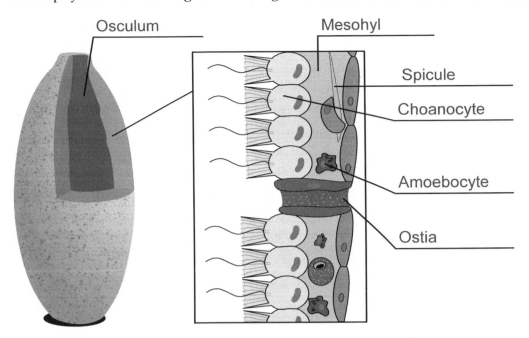

Osculum

Mesohyl

Spicule

Choanocyte

Amoebocyte

Ostia

53. Which phylum does this organism belong to? _Platyhelminthes_

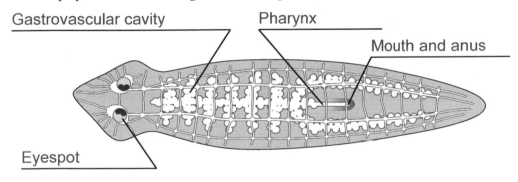

Gastrovascular cavity

Pharynx

Mouth and anus

Eyespot

54. Which phylum does this organism belong to? _Cnidaria_

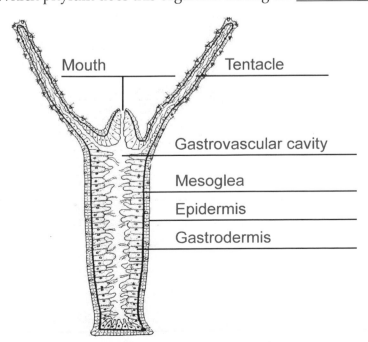

Mouth

Tentacle

Gastrovascular cavity

Mesoglea

Epidermis

Gastrodermis

CHAPTER 35 TEST: Mollusks and Annelids

Name:_____ Date: _____ Score: _____

Circle the best answer.

1. Which is not true concerning the general characteristics of mollusks?
   a. They are acoelomates.
   b. They exhibit bilateral symmetry.
   c. They undergo a trochophore stage.
   d. They use radula to acquire food.

2. Mollusk bodies are divided into two main regions. They are the
   a. Head and foot
   b. Visceral and dorsal chambers
   c. Visceral mass and head-foot
   d. Mantle and visceral chamber

3. Which region contains the mouth and sensory structures in a mollusk?
   a. Dorsal chamber
   b. Visceral mass
   c. Mantle
   d. Head

4. Which region contains the heart, digestive, reproductive, and excretory organs of a mollusk?
   a. Dorsal chamber
   b. Visceral mass
   c. Mantle
   d. Head

5. Which mollusk structure produces the hard valves or shells?
   a. Ganglia
   b. Visceral mass
   c. Radula
   d. Mantle

6. Paired clusters of nerve cells controlling the locomotion, feeding, and sensory processing are located
   a. Throughout the body of the mollusk
   b. In the head-foot and visceral mass
   c. In the mantle
   d. In the valves

7. A radula can be used to
   a. Reproduce
   b. Feed
   c. Locomote
   d. Produce energy

8. The process that occurs in gastropods to produce a head that can be retracted is called
   a. Trochophore
   b. Torsion
   c. Parapoda
   d. Clitellum

9. The largest and most diverse class of mollusks is ____.
   a. Gastropods
   b. Bivalves
   c. Cephalopods
   d. Polychaetes

10. Examples of gastropods are _____.
   a. Clams, oysters, and scallops
   b. Squids, nautiluses, octopuses
   c. Snails, conchs, and abalones
   d. Leeches, worms, and slugs

11. The structure of a land snail that acts as a modified lung is the _____.

    a. Mucous plug
    b. Mantle cavity
    c. Tentacle
    d. Hemolymph

12. The marine gastropod that has no shell is the _____.

    a. Nudibranch
    b. Octopus
    c. Squid
    d. Nautilus

13. Most bivalves are _____.

    a. Freely mobile
    b. Sessile
    c. Predators
    d. Freshwater inhabitants

14. The mantle cavity of a clam is sealed except for two fleshy tubes called _____.

    a. Valves
    b. Ganglia
    c. Tracts
    d. Siphons

15. Clams reproduce _____.

    a. Both sexually and asexually
    b. Sexually only
    c. Asexually only
    d. By parthenogenesis

16. Most cephalopods are _____.

    a. Sessile
    b. Free swimming
    c. Filter feeders
    d. Parasites

17. Which is not true about cephalopods and their nervous system?

    a. They have the largest brain of any invertebrate.
    b. They are capable of learning.
    c. They have eyespots that allow them to distinguish light but not shapes.
    d. Their tentacles have numerous sensory neurons.

18. Specialized pigment cells that allow a cephalopod to blend with its environment are called _____.

    a. Parapodia
    b. Chromatin
    c. Photophores
    d. Chromatophores

19. A squid usually has _____ tentacle(s) used for preying on and capturing food.

    a. 1
    b. 2
    c. 4
    d. 8

20. Architeuthis is the largest invertebrate. What is it?

    a. Giant Pacific octopus
    b. Chambered nautilus
    c. Giant Atlantic clam
    d. Giant squid

21. Which is not true of the chambered nautilus?

    a. It is the only cephalopod with an external shell.
    b. It has fluid-filled chambers that help with buoyancy as it discharges water.
    c. It uses only the outermost chamber of its shell for occupancy.
    d. It sheds its shell as it grows a new one..

22. The segmented coelom of the earthworm allows for _____.

    a. Asexual reproduction by the earthworm
    b. Muscle contraction producing locomotion independent from organ function
    c. Regeneration of organs in case of injury
    d. Coelomic fluid to more easily assist in digestion

23. The common characteristic that suggests mollusks and annelids are related is _____.

    a. The presence of a mantle

    b. Trochophore stage of development

    c. Setae and parapodia

    d. A one-way digestive system

24. The most commonly known oligochaete is the _____.

    a. Earthworm

    b. Leech

    c. Caterpillar

    d. Water eel

Put the digestive organs of the earthworm in order as food passes through them.

Anus	Crop	Esophagus	Gizzard	Intestine	Mouth	Pharynx

    a. Mouth

    b. Pharynx

    c. Esophagus

    d. Crop

    e. Gizzard

    f. Intestine

    g. Anus

Circle the best answer.

25. Contraction of which muscle in the earthworm causes the initial increase in pressure of the coelomic fluid initiating locomotion?

    a. Circular

    b. Longitudinal

    c. Adductor

    d. Segmental

26. Which *two* (choose 2) circulatory structures in the earthworm are responsible for pumping blood?

    a. Ventral blood vessel

    b. Dorsal blood vessel

    c. Aortic arches

    d. Peripheral blood vessels

27. An annelid is equipped with excretory tubules to eliminate excess water. These tubules are called

    a. Clitella

    b. Chromatophores

    c. Typhlosoles

    d. Nephridia

28. The clitellum is responsible for ____.

    a. Keeping the skin of the annelid moist for gas exchange

    b. Secreting mucous that aids in the reproductive process of the annelid

    c. Injecting a neurotoxin to paralyze its prey

    d. Eliminating excess water from the annelid's body

29. The largest class of annelids is ____.

    a. Oligochaeta

    b. Polychaeta

    c. Hirudinea

    d. Cephalopoda

30. The class of Hirudinea includes ____.

    a. Fireworms

    b. Flatworms

    c. Leeches

    d. Roundworms

31. Which statement is not true concerning leeches?

    a. They secrete an anesthetic so the host does not feel the leech.

    b. They can ingest ten times their own body weight in blood.

    c. They secrete an anticoagulant to keep the blood from clotting.

    d. They have numerous setae and parapodia for locomotion and attachment.

32. The majority of polychaetes ____.

    a. Are freshwater animals

    b. Are covered with numerous setae and parapodia

    c. Do not have a trochophore stage

    d. Are filter feeders and live on the ocean floor

Label the diagram.

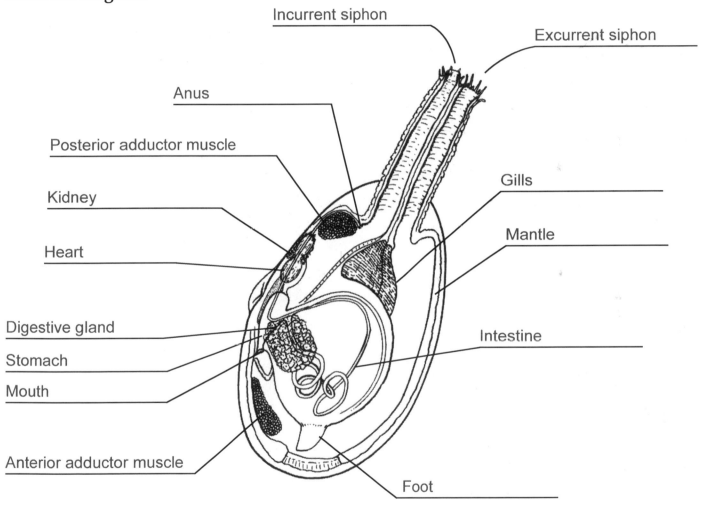

Incurrent siphon

Excurrent siphon

Anus

Posterior adductor muscle

Kidney

Heart

Gills

Mantle

Digestive gland

Stomach

Mouth

Intestine

Anterior adductor muscle

Foot

CHAPTERS 36-38 TEST: Invertebrates II

Name:_____ Date: _____ Score: _____

Circle the best answer.

1. Lobsters, crayfish, and shrimp are examples of _____.
   a. Arachnids
   b. Arthropods
   c. Crustaceans
   d. Both B and C

2. Spiders, ticks, and scorpions are classified as _____.
   a. Insects
   b. Crustaceans
   c. Arachnids
   d. Uropods

3. The anterior body segment of a crustacean or spider is called the _____.
   a. Head
   b. Telson
   c. Uropod
   d. Cephalothorax

4. The appendages on either side of a spider's mouth with which it manipulates its food are the _____.
   a. Pedipalps
   b. Chelicerae
   c. Maxilla
   d. Mandibles

5. The respiratory organs found in most crustaceans are called _____.
   a. Gills
   b. Spiracles
   c. Book lungs
   d. Trachea

6. The short, fingerlike organs of a spider's abdomen with which it spins silk are the _____.
   a. Pedipalps
   b. Chelicerae
   c. Spinnerets
   d. Pelicles

7. The excretory organs of a crayfish are _____.
   a. Malpighian tubes
   b. Green glands
   c. Renal tubules
   d. Nephridia

8. The subphylum of extinct arthropods is _____.
   a. Myriapoda
   b. Trilobita
   c. Chelicerata
   d. Hexapoda

9. Most aquatic arthropods are categorized into which subphylum?
   a. Myriapoda
   b. Chilopoda
   c. Crustacea
   d. Diplopoda

10. Spiders use which of the below structures for respiration?
    a. Malpighian tubules
    b. Book lungs
    c. Gills
    d. Spiracles

11. A free-swimming crustacean larva is called a _____.
    a. Trochophore
    b. Statocyst
    c. Nauplius
    d. Barnacle

12. Fused body segments that are usually specialized for a specific function are called _____.
    a. Rostra
    b. Tagmata
    c. Antennules
    d. Uropods

13. Terrestrial crustaceans that lack adaptations for water (e.g., pill bugs) are classed as _____.
    a. Uropods
    b. Decapods
    c. Ostia
    d. Isopods

14. The appendages with pincers found on the crayfish are called _____.
    a. Swimmerets
    b. Ostia
    c. Maxillipeds
    d. Chelipeds

15. The five ventral appendages found on a crayfish abdomen are called _____.
    a. Pedicel
    b. Ostia
    c. Maxillipeds
    d. Swimmerets

16. Examples of other crustaceans include _____.
    a. Shrimp, barnacles, and water fleas
    b. Harvestmen, ticks, mites, and spiders
    c. Annelids, nematodes, and rotifers
    d. Brown recluse, black widow, and sac spiders

17. How many different types of spiders in the U.S. are poisonous to humans?
    a. 2
    b. 4
    c. 6
    d. 8

18. These dangerous arachnids cause Lyme disease and Rocky Mountain spotted fever.
    a. Mites
    b. Scorpions
    c. Ticks
    d. Chiggers

19. The organs located on the abdomen of a grasshopper used for breathing are called _____.
    a. Lungs
    b. Trachea
    c. Nematocytes
    d. Spiracles

20. Insects are in the subphylum _____.
    a. Hexapoda
    b. Insecta
    c. Arthropoda
    d. Trilobita

21. Which body segment of an insect has the legs and wings attached to it?
    a. Mouth
    b. Thorax
    c. Abdomen
    d. Head

22. Honeybees that develop from unfertilized eggs are called _____.
    a. Workers
    b. Queens
    c. Nurse bees
    d. Drones

23. A grasshopper's exoskeleton is covered by a waxy cuticle secreted by the _____.
    a. Exoskeleton
    b. Dermis
    c. Epidermis
    d. Endoskeleton

24. Insect mouthparts that function as upper and lower cutting tools are the _____.
    a. Labrum and labium
    b. Maxilla and mandibless
    c. Salivary structures
    d. Chelicerae

25. Which characteristic does an insect not share with members of the subphylum Myriapoda?
    a. Mandibles
    b. Unbranched appendages
    c. Metamorphosis
    d. One pair of antennae

26. These insects most often live in large colonies.
    a. Hymenopterans
    b. Odonatans
    c. Lepidopterans
    d. Orthopterans

27. The large oval membrane that covers the air-filled cavity on the sides of the abdominal cavity and conducts sound in a grasshopper is called the _____.
    a. Malpighian tubule
    b. Ovipositor
    c. Spiracle
    d. Tympanum

28. A type of passive insect defense whereby harmless insects mimic dangerous insects with special warning coloration is called _____.
    a. Mullerian mimicry
    b. Batesian mimicry
    c. Camo mimicry
    d. Exoskeleton

29. The dances of the bees studied by Karl von Frisch explain how bees _____.
    a. Attract a mate
    b. Warn the hive of danger
    c. Choose a queen
    d. Communicate the location of food

30. A worker bee's ovipositor is used for _____ purposes only.
    a. Defense
    b. Food gathering
    c. Reproduction
    d. Exoskeleton

31. Adult echinoderms develop from larvae that are _____.
    a. Sessile
    b. Radially symmetrical
    c. Bilaterally symmetrical
    d. Protostomes

32. Which is not true of echinoderms?
    a. They are deuterostomes.
    b. They are acoelomates.
    c. They undergo indeterminate cleavage.
    d. They exhibit no cephalization.

33. Sea lilies and feather stars are part of the class of echinoderms known as _____.
    a. Crinoidea
    b. Echinoidea
    c. Ophiuroidea
    d. Holothuroidea
    e. Asteroidea

34. The class of echinoderms that includes sea urchins is the class _____.
    a. Crinoidea
    b. Echinoidea
    c. Ophiuroidea
    d. Holothuroidea
    e. Asteroidea

35. One characteristic that is found only in echinoderms is _____.
    a. A nerve net
    b. The presence of only two tissue layers during development
    c. A water-vascular system
    d. An endoskeleton

36. The surface that is opposite the mouth in a sea star is the _____.
    a. Oral surface
    b. Aboral surface
    c. Dorsal surface
    d. Posterior surface

37. Animals in the subphyla Urochordata and Cephalochordata live _____.
    a. Only in fresh water
    b. Only in the ocean
    c. Only on land
    d. Fresh water, marine, and on land

38. The subphylum of echinoderms that includes sea cucumbers is the _____.
  a. Crinoidea
  b. Echinoidea
  c. Ophiuroidea
  d. Holothuroidea
  e. Asteroidea

39. The tiny pincers surrounding the spines on many species of Asteroidea are called _____.
  a. Chellicerata
  b. Pedicellariae
  c. Ampulla
  d. Madreporite

40. The digestive structure that can be extended externally to digest food in a sea star is the _____.
  a. Cardiac stomach
  b. Pyloric stomach
  c. Ampulla
  d. Madreporite

41. The tube that connects the madreporite to the tube encircling the mouth is the _____.
  a. Stone canal
  b. Ring canal
  c. Central canal
  d. Radial canal

42. Contraction of the muscles around the _____ causes the tube feet to fill and extend.
  a. Ampulla
  b. Eyespot
  c. Ring canal
  d. Stone canal

43. Most sea stars eat _____.
  a. Plankton
  b. Seaweed
  c. Clams and mollusks
  d. Small fish

44. Gas exchange occurs through _____ in a sea star.
  a. Osmosis
  b. Trachea
  c. Diffusion
  d. Gills

45. The free-swimming larvae of a sea star are called _____.
  a. Bipinnaria
  b. Tunicates
  c. Lancelets
  d. Nauplius

46. Reproduction and fertilization in the subphylum Asteroidea occur _____.
  a. Externally
  b. Internally
  c. Hermaphroditically
  d. Asexually

Write the correct letter in the blank before each numbered item.

A. Centipede   **B.** Millipede   **C.** Both

___A___ 47. Poisonous

___A___ 48. One pair of legs per body segment

___B___ 49. Class Diplopoda

___B___ 50. Slow movers

___B___ 51. Round bodies

___B___ 52. Detritivores

___A___ 53. One pair of long jointed antennae

___C___ 54. Live in dark moist places

___C___ 55. Phylum Myriapoda

___A___ 56. Carnivores

List the three different ways insects communicate within their species.

57. <u>Pheromones</u>

58. <u>Sounds</u>

59. <u>Lights</u>

Write the correct letter in the blank before each numbered item.

<u>I</u> **60.** Coleoptera

<u>H</u> **61.** Orthoptera

<u>F</u> **62.** Diptera

<u>G</u> **63.** Odonata

<u>D</u> **64.** Hymenoptera

<u>E</u> **65.** Isoptera

<u>B</u> **66.** Lepidoptera

<u>C</u> **67.** Homoptera

<u>A</u> **68.** Hemiptera

A. Stinkbugs

B. Butterflies

C. Cicadas

D. Bees

E. Termites

F. Mosquitoes

G. Dragonflies

H. Grasshoppers

I. Ladybugs

Answer the following question.

69. Describe the components and functions of an echinoderm's water-vascular system. (3 pts.)

<u>Water flows in through the madreporite and proceeds through the canals to the ampulla.</u>

<u>Muscles around the ampulla contract, pushing water into the tube feet and causing them</u>

<u>to extend. Muscles in the tube feet contract to push the water back up into the ampulla,</u>

<u>retracting the tube feet.</u>

Correctly label the diagram and answer the question below.

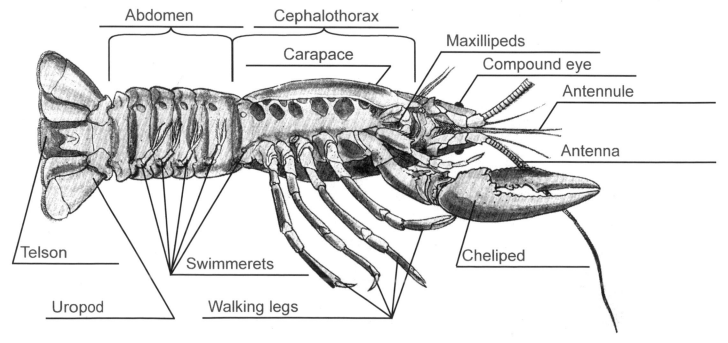

70. What phylum does this organism belong to? <u>Arthropoda</u>

Correctly label the diagram and answer the question below.

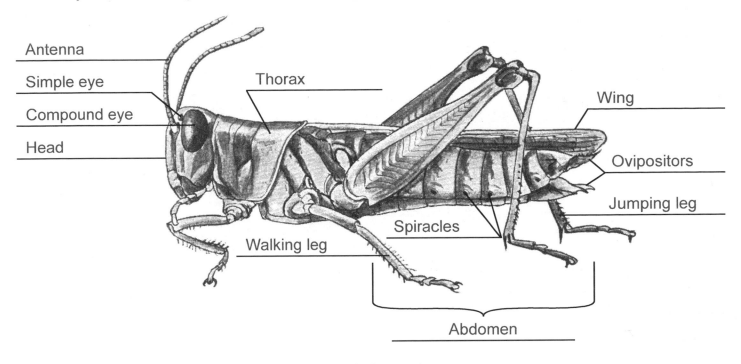

Antenna

Simple eye

Compound eye

Head

Thorax

Wing

Ovipositors

Jumping leg

Spiracles

Walking leg

Abdomen

71. What phylum does this organism belong to? Arthropoda

Answer the questions below.

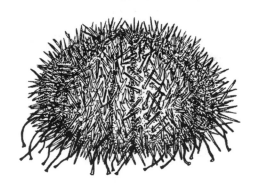

72. What phylum does this organism belong to?

Echinodermata

73. What phylum does this organism belong to?

Echinodermata

FINAL EXAM

Name:_____ Date: _____ Score: _____

Circle the best answer.

1. Biology is the study of _____.
   a. Animals
   b. Plants
   c. All living things
   d. None of the above

2. What is the smallest known unit that exhibits all of the characteristics of life?
   a. Atom
   b. Molecule
   c. Cell
   d. Organism

3. Which is not one of the seven characteristics of life?
   a. Responds to stimuli
   b. Natural selection
   c. Growth and development
   d. Homeostasis

4. What are the products in the hydrolysis of ATP?
   a. Water, ATP, and phosphate
   b. Energy, ADP, and phosphate
   c. AMP and two phosphates
   d. Water, ADP, and phosphate

5. How many covalent bonds is carbon able to form?
   a. 2
   b. 4
   c. 6
   d. 8

6. Organic molecules that catalyze reactions in living systems are called
   a. Macromolecules
   b. Proteins
   c. Enzymes
   d. All of the above

7. Which is not one of the four major macromolecules of life?
   a. Proteins
   b. Lipids
   c. Nucleic acids
   d. Minerals

8. What is the monomer of a carbohydrate?
   a. Amino acid
   b. Monosaccharide
   c. Polysaccharide
   d. Nucleotide

9. What is the storage form of glucose in animals?
   a. Cellulose
   b. Starch
   c. Glycogen
   d. Fructose

10. Glucose, fructose, and galactose all have the same chemical formula but are different compounds called _____.
    a. Isomers
    b. Isotopes
    c. Ions
    d. Homologues

11. Which reaction occurs to bond monomers into polymers?
    a. Condensation
    b. Hydrolysis
    c. Combustion
    d. Oxidation

12. How many different types of monomers are found in proteins?
    a. 17
    b. 20
    c. 50
    d. 100

13. What is the purpose of ATP in cells?

    a. Catalyze reactions
    b. Provide energy
    c. Protein synthesis
    d. Photosynthesis

14. Which structure would not be found in a prokaryote?

    a. Nucleus
    b. Ribosome
    c. Cytoplasm
    d. Plasmid

15. Which organelle performs the function of photosynthesis in a plant?

    a. Ribosome
    b. Mitochondria
    c. Thylakoid
    d. Chloroplast

16. Which molecule(s) are found in the cell membrane?

    a. Phospholipids
    b. Mitochondria
    c. ATP
    d. Plastids

17. Which scientist developed cell theory and named cells after the rooms of a monastery?

    a. Gregor Mendel
    b. Anton van Leeuwenhoek
    c. Robert Hooke
    d. Louis Pasteur

18. Cells are microscopic in size to _____ the surface area relative to their volume.

    a. Decrease
    b. Increase
    c. Repair
    d. Flatten

19. What is one of the primary functions of the plasma membrane?

    a. Controls what moves into and out of the cell
    b. DNA replication
    c. Protein synthesis
    d. Phagocytosis

20. Which is the eukaryotic organelle responsible for packaging and exporting proteins?

    a. Rough endoplasmic reticulum
    b. Smooth endoplasmic reticulum
    c. Lysosome
    d. Nucleus

21. The movement of water through a cell membrane is called _____.

    a. Osmosis
    b. Diffusion
    c. Facilitated diffusion
    d. Active transport

22. Which is not a type of passive transport?

    a. Osmosis
    b. Diffusion
    c. Facilitated diffusion
    d. Exocytosis

23. Why is active transport considered to be an active rather than a passive process?

    a. It moves substances down their concentration gradient.
    b. It requires energy..
    c. It moves substances that readily diffuse across the plasma membrane.
    d. More than one of the above

Use the diagram below to answer the questions. The membrane is permeable to glucose.

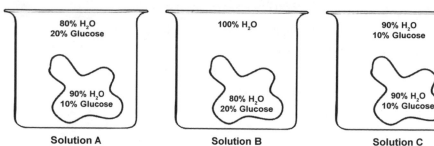

80% H_2O 20% Glucose	100% H_2O	90% H_2O 10% Glucose
90% H_2O 10% Glucose	80% H_2O 20% Glucose	90% H_2O 10% Glucose
Solution A	**Solution B**	**Solution C**

24. Will water move into or out of the sac in solution A? _____Out_____

25. Which direction will the solute move in example A, assuming the membrane is permeable? _____Into_____

26. Will the solute move into or out of the sac in solution B, assuming the membrane is permeable? _____Out_____

27. Will water move into or out of the sac in solution C? _____Both_____

28. The cell (the bag) in solution B will likely undergo a process called _____cytolysis_____.

Circle the best answer.

29. What is the purpose of crossing-over in eukaryotic cells?
    a. Minimize mutations
    b. Ensure genetic variability
    c. Ensure natural selection
    d. Aid in metabolism

30. During which phase of the cell cycle are some cells complete and so exit the cycle?
    a. S
    b. G_1
    c. G_2
    d. G_0

31. During cell division, the DNA of a eukaryotic cell is tightly packed and coiled into _____.
    a. Chromatin
    b. Histones
    c. Chromosomes
    d. Centrioles

32. If an organism has diploid number of 28, what will its haploid number be?
    a. 56
    b. 102
    c. 14
    d. 7

33. Most prokaryotic cells reproduce by a process called _____.
    a. Meiosis
    b. Parthenogenesis
    c. Regeneration
    d. Binary or multiple fission

34. What are homologues?
    a. Two similar chromosomes that carry the same traits, one from each parent
    b. The same thing as an allele
    c. Monohybrids
    d. Identical chromatids

35. The end result of mitosis is _____.
    a. Two cells identical to the parent cell (s)
    b. Two cells similar to the parent cell (s)
    c. Four different sperm cells
    d. One egg and four polar bodies

36. What occurs during crossing-over?
    a. Chromatids separate at the centromere.
    b. Spindle fibers attach to the homologues.
    c. Genes transfer from one homologue to another.
    d. DNA replicates and forms chromatids.

37. Haploid cells are formed for the first time during which phase?

a. Prophase

b. Prophase I

c. Prophase II

d. None of the above

38. An organism that is homozygous recessive will have which genotype?

a. BB

b. Bb

c. bb

d. BbBb

39. Mendel named his true-breeding generation of pea plants _____.

a. P

b. F

c. F_1

d. F_2

40. When an organism is heterozygous for a trait, it has _____.

a. Inherited the same dominant alleles from both parents

b. Inherited one dominant allele and one recessive allele from the parents

c. Inherited the same recessive alleles from both parents

d. Inherited no alleles from its parents

41. In a monohybrid cross between a homozygous dominant parent and a homozygous recessive parent, one would predict the phenotype ratio of offspring to be _____.

a. 2:2

b. 4:1

c. 4:0

d. 1:2:1

42. In a monohybrid cross between two heterozygous parents, one would expect the genotype ratio offspring to be _____.

a. 2:2

b. 4:1

c. 4:0

d. 1:2:1

43. The purpose of a testcross is to _____.

a. Ensure genetic variability

b. Determine the phenotype of a dominant genotype

c. Determine the genotype of a dominant phenotype

d. Ensure true-breeding parents for future crosses

44. During a testcross, the organism in question would be crossed with a _____.

a. Homozygous dominant

b. Homozygous recessive

c. Heterozygous

d. Incomplete dominant

45. Who was the father of genetics?

a. Mendel

b. Hooke

c. Leeuwenhoek

d. Pasteur

46. Which is not true concerning the father of genetics?

a. He was a monk.

b. He was German.

c. He was a gardener.

d. He studied statistics.

47. Draw a Punnett square of a monohybrid cross between a purple-flowering pea plant and a white-flowering pea plant with an F_1 generation whose offspring are 50% purple plants and 50% white plants.

	p	p
P	Pp	Pp
p	pp	pp

48. During the synthesis of protein, new mRNA is made by what process?

a. Replication

b. Transcription

c. Translation

d. Synapsis

49. Complementary base-pairing rules of DNA replication state that bases complementary to adenine and guanine pair respectively with _____ and _____.
    a. Uracil and cytosine
    b. Thymine and cytosine
    c. Cytosine and thymine
    d. Guanine and thymine

50. Base-pairing rules dictate in DNA replication that a strand of DNA with the base sequence of GTAATCATG will form an opposite base sequence of _____.
    a. CUTTUGAUG
    b. GTAATCATG
    c. CAUUAGUAC
    d. CATTAGTAC

51. If the percentage of guanine on a DNA strand is 20%, what will the percentage of adenine be?
    a. 20
    b. 60
    c. 30
    d. 80

52. Which would not be found in a molecule of nucleic acid?
    a. Deoxyribose
    b. Adenosine
    c. Phosphate
    d. Cytosine

53. Amino acids are assembled based on instructions encoded in the sequence of nucleotides on the _____.
    a. mRNA
    b. DNA
    c. tRNA
    d. All of the above

54. In eukaryotic cells, translation takes place in/on the _____.
    a. Ribosome
    b. Nucleus
    c. Nucleoid
    d. Nucleolus

55. A tRNA with the anticodon GCA will bond with the codon _____.
    a. CGT
    b. GCU
    c. CGU
    d. GCT

56. In prokaryotic cells, DNA replication takes place in/on the _____.
    a. Ribosome
    b. Nucleus
    c. Nucleolus
    d. Nucleoid

57. A mutation is _____.
    a. A gene sequence that produces a disease or disorder
    b. A gene sequence that is different than the parent gene
    c. A gene sequence that improves a species
    d. The formation of free radicals

58. Which structure would you not find in a bacterial cell?
    a. Ribosome
    b. Plasmid
    c. Lysosome
    d. DNA

59. How do bacteria become resistant to antibiotics?
    a. Mutating their cell wall
    b. Changing their shape
    c. Acquiring a plasmid
    d. Forming an endospore

60. Where would you most likely find a thermoacidophile?
    a. Salty environment
    b. Anaerobic environment
    c. Hot acidic environment
    d. In the intestines of other organisms

61. Where would you likely find enteric bacteria?
    a. Salty environment
    b. Anaerobic environment
    c. Hot acidic environment
    d. In the intestines of organisms

62. How do photoautotrophic bacteria obtain energy?

   a. Sun

   b. Other organisms

   c. Chemicals

   d. Active transport

63. Which is true concerning obligate anaerobes?

   a. They need oxygen to survive.

   b. They can live with or without oxygen.

   c. They cannot survive in the presence of oxygen.

   d. They must have sunshine to survive.

64. Many bacteria have pili that aid in the process of _____.

   a. Transformation

   b. Remediation

   c. Conjugation

   d. Transduction

65. Which prokaryotes are thought to be largely responsible for establishing the Earth's oxygen-rich atmosphere?

   a. Nitrogen fixing

   b. Cyanobacteria

   c. Blue-green algae

   d. Spirogyra

66. What is the purpose of nitrogen fixation?

   a. Convert atmospheric nitrogen into soil nitrate for plants

   b. Convert ammonia into nitrogen for the soil

   c. Convert soil nitrites into nitrogen

   d. None of the above

67. A Gram-negative bacteria stains ____ because it has a ____ amount of peptidoglycan in its cell wall.

   a. Purple, large

   b. Purple, small

   c. Pink, large

   d. Pink, small

68. Antibiotics attack bacteria by _____.

   a. Interfering with mitosis

   b. Interfering with cell wall formation

   c. Interfering with protein synthesis

   d. All of the above

69. The purpose of the endospore inside a bacterium is to _____.

   a. Help in the resistance of host immunity

   b. Allow it to acquire a plasmid

   c. Help it adhere to other bacteria and host tissue

   d. Allow it to regenerate if it is destroyed

70. DNA that helps to make bacteria antibiotic resistant are called _____.

   a. Endospores

   b. Pili

   c. Capsids

   d. Plasmids

71. Most foodborne illness is transmitted through _____.

   a. Contaminated water

   b. Skin lesions

   c. Body fluids

   d. Undercooked meat

72. Which is not one of the three primary bacterial shapes?

   a. Bacillus

   b. Icosahedral

   c. Cocci

   d. Spirillum

What are the four characteristics that all animals exhibit at some point in their life cycle?

73. Multicellular

74. Heterotrophic

75. Reproduce sexually

76. Movement

What are the three embryonic germ layers in any order? What main organs or tissues do they become? (2 pts. each)

77. Mesoderm: Bones, muscles, circulatory system

78. Ectoderm: Skin, hair, nails, nervous system

79. Endoderm: Gut and most visceral organs

Circle the best answer.

80. The cell division that takes place immediately following fertilization is termed _____.
    a. Cleavage
    b. Blastula formation
    c. Gastrulation
    d. Organogenesis

81. The fluid-filled cavity that forms following gastrulation is called the _____.
    a. Archenteron
    b. Blastocoel
    c. Coelom
    d. Blastopore

82. Most vertebrate embryos that are hatched or born undergo which type of development?
    a. Direct
    b. Indirect
    c. Determinate
    d. Indeterminate

83. The deep cavity that becomes the gut during embryonic development is the _____.
    a. Archenteron
    b. Blastocoel
    c. Coelom
    d. Blastopore

84. Animals that have no body cavity and are solid tissue are called _____.
    a. Acoelomates
    b. Pseudocoelomates
    c. Coelomates
    d. None of the above

85. The fate of the blastopore in a protostome is to become the _____.
    a. Brain
    b. Mouth
    c. Belly button
    d. Anus

86. When the fate of a cell is fixed late in its development, the cleavage is said to be _____.
    a. Direct
    b. Indirect
    c. Determinate
    d. Indeterminate

87. The process of coelom formation in protostomes is called _____.
    a. Enterocoely
    b. Schizocoely
    c. Plasmocoely
    d. Schizophrenia

Match the phylum name on the left with the organism in that phylum on the right.

__D__	88. Rotifera	A.	Octopus
__I__	89. Porifera	B.	Jellyfish
__G__	90. Nematoda	C.	Flatworm
__C__	91. Platyhelminthes	D.	Rotifer
__F__	92. Annelida	E.	Sea star
__B__	93. Cnidaria	F.	Segmented worm
__E__	94. Echinodermata	G.	Roundworm
__A__	95. Mollusca	H.	Lobster
__H__	96. Arthropoda	I.	Sponge

Circle the best answer.

97. Protists are thought to have evolved from ancient prokaryotes as two prokaryotes lived _____.

   a. Parasitically

   b. Endosymbiotically

   c. Enterically

   d. Pathologically

98. The internal flowing of an organism's cytoplasm is called _____.

   a. Amebiasis

   b. Cytokinesis

   c. Cytoplasmic streaming

   d. Pseudopodia

99. Protists in which phylum have no means of locomotion in their adult form?

   a. Ciliophora

   b. Apicomplexa

   c. Sarcomastigophora

   d. Protozoa

100. Pigments that trap light in green algae are called _____.

   a. Chloroplasts

   b. Thylakoids

   c. Chlorophylls

   d. Pyrenoids

101. Diatoms are unicellular protists from which phylum?

   a. Phaeophyta

   b. Bacillariophyta

   c. Dinoflagellata

   d. Chlorophyta

102. Protists from the phylum Myxomycota are also known as _____.

   a. Water molds

   b. Plasmodial slime molds

   c. Cellular slime molds

   d. Fruiting bodies

103. Funguslike protists will generally form fruiting bodies when _____.

   a. They get hungry and thirsty.

   b. They run out of food and water.

   c. The weather turns cold.

   d. All of the above

104. Why are plantlike protists classified as protists and not plants?

   a. They are not photosynthetic.

   b. They have no true roots, stems, or leaves..

   c. They are not eukaryotes.

   d. They have no means of obtaining carbon dioxide.

105. Once inside a cell, what enzyme allows a retrovirus to produce thousands of new viruses?

a. Retrovirase
b. RNAscriptase
c. Reverse transcriptase
d. Retrolyase

What are three effective measures in viral disease prevention or treatment?

106. Antivirals

107. Vector control

108. Vaccinations

Circle the best answer.

109. How is the viral lytic cycle different from the lysogenic cycle?

a. The lytic cycle allows a virus to lie dormant for months or years.
b. The lytic cycle begins viral replication immediately on access to a cell.
c. The lytic cycle inserts its genome into the host cell genome before it replicates.
d. The lytic cycle is less virulent than the lysogenic cycle.

110. A viral disease that occurs in childhood and may reappear in adulthood in different form is _____.

a. Smallpox
b. Chickenpox
c. Whooping cough
d. Measles

111. Viral hepatitis most commonly affects which organ?

a. Intestines
b. Spleen
c. Gallbladder
d. Liver

Answer the following questions.

112. For what is HIV an acronym? Human immunodeficiency virus

113. For what is AIDS an acronym? Acquired immune deficiency syndrome

Circle the best answer.

114. The common jellyfish moves from the blastula stage to a ciliated larva called a _____.

a. Trochophore
b. Gemmule
c. Planula
d. Bud

115. The jellylike substance between the two cell layers of the cnidarian is the _____.

a. Mesohyl
b. Goo
c. Mesoglea
d. Mesoderm

116. Bell-shaped cnidarians specialized for swimming have this body form.
   a. Polyp
   b. Hydra
   c. Flippers
   d. Medusa

117. Cells that crawl around the body of a sponge and pick up and deliver nutrients are the _____.
   a. Choanocytes
   b. Amoebocytes
   c. Epidermal cells
   d. Phagocytes

118. The long coiled filament organelle specialized for paralyzing and capturing prey is a _____.
   a. Physalia
   b. Cnidocyte
   c. Nematocoil
   d. Nematocyst

119. The sea anemone and coral belong to which class of cnidarians?
   a. Anthozoa
   b. Cubozoa
   c. Hydrozoa
   d. Scyphozoa

120. Why do flatworms have no need for circulatory or respiratory systems?
   a. They have cells that carry oxygen and nutrients to the cells.
   b. They are not really alive.
   c. They are flat so that all cells are near the surface for gas exchange..
   d. They use other systems for gas exchange.

121. Which system helps planarians deal with osmotic water?
   a. Circulatory
   b. Respiratory
   c. Excretory
   d. Nervous

122. The primary hosts of Taenia saginatus are _____.
   a. Cows
   b. Pigs
   c. Snails
   d. Humans

123. How do most trematodes gain access to a human host?
   a. Through contaminated food or water
   b. Undercooked meat
   c. Skin
   d. Body fluids

124. Each mature tapeworm proglottid primarily contains _____.
   a. Waste
   b. Food
   c. Eggs
   d. Nephridia

125. What developmental feature indicates that echinoderms are more closely related to vertebrates?
   a. They have a similar morphology.
   b. They are both protostomes.
   c. They are both deuterostomes.
   d. They undergo the same type of cleavage.

126. Mollusk bodies are divided into two main regions. They are the
   a. Head and foot
   b. Visceral and dorsal chambers
   c. Visceral mass and head-foot
   d. Mantle and visceral chamber

127. Which mollusk structure produces the hard valves or shells?
   a. Ganglia
   b. Visceral mass
   c. Radula
   d. Mantle

128. The process occurring in gastropods to produce a head that can be retracted is called

    a. Trochophore

    b. Torsion

    c. Parapoda

    d. Clitellum

129. The largest and most diverse class of mollusks is

    a. Gastropods

    b. Bivalves

    c. Cephalopods

    d. Polychaetes

130. Examples of gastropods are

    a. Clams, oysters, and scallops

    b. Squids, nautiluses, octopuses

    c. Snails, conchs, and abaloness

    d. Leeches, worms, and slugs

131. The mantle cavity of a clam is sealed except for two fleshy tubes called

    a. Valves

    b. Ganglia

    c. Tracts

    d. Siphons

132. Clams reproduce

    a. Both sexually and asexually

    b. Sexually only

    c. Asexually only

    d. By binary fission

133. Most cephalopods are

    a. Sessile

    b. Free swimming

    c. Filter feeders

    d. Parasites

134. Which is not true relative to the nervous system of a cephalopod?

    a. They have the largest brain of any invertebrate.

    b. They are capable of learning.

    c. They have eyespots that allow them to distinguish light but not shapes..

    d. Their tentacles have numerous sensory neurons.

135. The common characteristic that suggests mollusks and annelids are related is

    a. The presence of a mantle

    b. Trochophore stage of development

    c. Setae and parapodia

    d. A one-way digestive system

136. The most commonly known oligochaete is the

    a. Earthworm

    b. Leech

    c. Caterpillar

    d. Water eel

Place the digestive organs of the earthworm in order as food passes through them.
Anus, Mouth, Gizzard, Pharynx, Esophagus, Crop, Long intestine

137. Mouth

138. Pharynx

139. Esophagus

140. Crop

141. Gizzard

142. Long intestine

143. Anus

Circle the best answer.

144. Contraction of which muscle in the earthworm causes the initial increase in pressure of the coelomic fluid and ultimately locomotion?
    a. Circular
    b. Longitudinal
    c. Adductor
    d. Segmental

145. What are the two main circulatory structures in the earthworm responsible for pumping blood?
    a. Ventral and dorsal blood vessels
    b. Dorsal blood vessel and aortic arches
    c. Aortic arches and ventral blood vessel
    d. Peripheral blood vessels and heart

146. An annelid is equipped with excretory tubules to eliminate excess water. These tubules are called
    a. Clitella
    b. Chromatophores
    c. Typhlosoles
    d. Nephridia

147. The clitellum of an annelid is responsible for
    a. Keeping the skin of the annelid moist for gas exchange
    b. Secreting mucous that aids in the reproductive process of the annelid
    c. Injecting a neurotoxin to paralyze its prey
    d. Eliminating excess water from the annelid's body

148. The movement of sugar in a plant from its place of production to its place of storage is _____.
    a. Cohesion-tension
    b. Transpiration
    c. Evaporation
    d. Translocation

149. The opening and closing of stomata are regulated by the presence of which mineral?
    a. Sodium
    b. Potassium
    c. Magnesium
    d. Chlorine

150. The three basic organs of a plant are _____.
    a. Dermal, ground, and vascular
    b. Roots, stems, and leaves
    c. Parenchyma, collenchyma, and sclerenchyma
    d. Tracheids, vessel elements, and sieve tube members

151. The plant structure found on the end of a stem or root where cells continuously divide is
    a. Apical meristem
    b. Intercalary meristem
    c. Lateral meristem
    d. Bud scales

152. Secondary growth in plants occurs from which structure?
    a. Apical meristem
    b. Intercalary meristem
    c. Lateral meristem
    d. Bud scales

153. Water movement from the plant roots up the stem relies on which two properties?
    a. Osmosis and diffusion
    b. Tension and attraction
    c. Cohesion and adhesion
    d. Transpiration and evaporation

154. The process by which a plant moves water up and then loses it is called _____.
    a. Transpiration
    b. Cohesion
    c. Adhesion
    d. Diffusion

155. In a stem cross section, an annual ring represents an abrupt change between
    a. Summerwood and springwood
    b. Heartwood and sapwood
    c. Bark and cork
    d. Xylem and phloem

156. The driving force for transpiration is provided by
   a. Water pressure in the roots
   b. Water tension in the stems
   c. Evaporation of water from the leaves
   d. The hydrolysis of ATP

157. Most aquatic arthropods are categorized into which subphylum?
   a. Myriapoda
   b. Chilopoda
   c. Crustacea
   d. Diplopoda

158. Spiders use which of the below structures for respiration?
   a. Malpighian tubules
   b. Book lungs
   c. Gills
   d. Spiracles

159. A free-swimming crustacean larva is called a ____.
   a. Trochophore
   b. Statocyst
   c. Nauplius
   d. Barnacle

160. Fused body segments that are usually specialized for a specific function are called ____.
   a. Rostra
   b. Tagmata
   c. Antennules
   d. Uropods

161. The organs located on the abdomen of a grasshopper used for breathing are called ____.
   a. Lungs
   b. Trachea
   c. Nematocytes
   d. Spiracles

162. Insects are in the subphylum ____.
   a. Hexapoda
   b. Insecta
   c. Arthropoda
   d. Trilobita

163. Which body segment of an insect has the legs and wings attached to it?
   a. Mouth
   b. Thorax
   c. Abdomen
   d. Head

164. Honeybees that develop from unfertilized eggs are called ____.
   a. Workers
   b. Queens
   c. Nurse bees
   d. Drones

165. A grasshopper's exoskeleton is covered by a waxy cuticle secreted by the ____.
   a. Exoskeleton
   b. Dermis
   c. Epidermis
   d. Endoskeleton

List the compounds used to Gram stain bacteria in the order they are used.

166. Crystal violet

167. Iodine

168. Alcohol or acetone

169. Safranin

170. Describe in detail the structure, elements, and function of a chromosome. (8 pts.)

A chromosome preparing for mitosis is made up of two identical chromatids held together by a centromere. Each chromatid is made up of strands of DNA, tightly packed and coiled with the help of histones. DNA is a double-stranded helix of nucleotides covalently bonded together. The two complementary strands are held together by hydrogen bonds. Chromosomes form when a cell is beginning to replicate, and their purpose is to pass the entire genetic code of the organism to the new cell.

171. Why are mitochondria important to the functioning of muscle cells in eukaryotes? (2 pts.)

Muscle cells use lots of energy. Mitochondria convert glucose into ATP, which is the form of energy the cells require to function. Muscle cells need abundant mitochondria for energy.

172. Explain the purpose of a sodium-potassium pump and its mechanism. (8 pts.)

The purpose of the sodium-potassium pump is to establish an electrical gradient, which helps to set up and maintain membrane permeability. This helps membranes control how and when substances cross. Three sodium bind to the pump inside the cell. One molecule of ATP is cleaved into ADP and one phosphate, which stays bound to the pump. The three NA+ ions move into the pump. The protein pump shields the Na+ from the bilayer and releases them outside the cell. Two K+ ions bind to the pump, travel through it, and are released inside the cell. The phosphate group is released, and the process begins again.

Correctly label the diagram.

Nucleolus

Nucleus

Lysosome

Plasma membrane

BONUS

Mitochondrion

Golgi

Ribosome

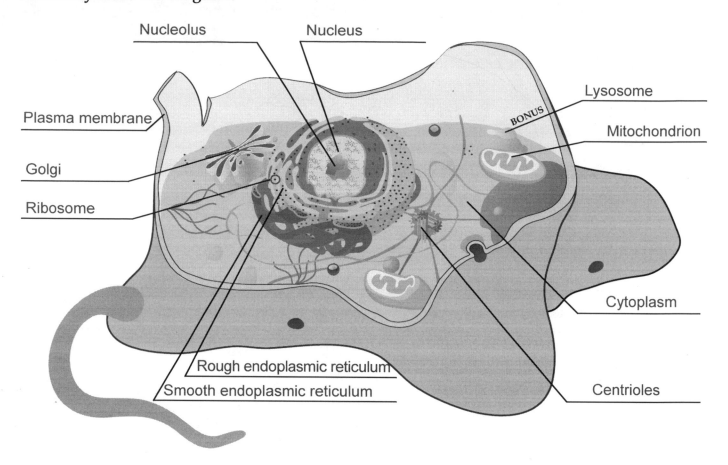

Cytoplasm

Rough endoplasmic reticulum

Smooth endoplasmic reticulum

Centrioles